WHAT IS
ATOMIC ENERGY?

All the above volumes are fully
illustrated and uniform
with this book.

6s.

net.

WHAT IS
ATOMIC ENERGY?

K. MENDELSSOHN
M.A., Ph.D., F.Inst.P.

Line drawings in the text by
VICTOR REINGANUM
and the AUTHOR

SIGMA

Sigma Introduction to Science 3

SIGMA BOOKS LTD.,
7, John St., London,
W.C.1.

First Published 1946.

To J. L. C.

Printed by J. B. Mackie & Co., Ltd., 98 St. Margaret St., Dunfermline

PREFACE

The first announcement of the release of atomic energy was not made in a scientific journal, nor even through the newspapers or the radio. It came in the form of unparalleled destruction which on August 6th, 1945 descended on the town of Hiroshima. A world which had been numbed by the horrors of scientific weapons, which after the greatest war of destruction ever waged was timidly beginning to look forward to an age of peace, accepted this latest present of science with a dull sense of fear and foreboding. The general feeling of uneasiness was increased by the Press which stressed the extreme secrecy of the invention. It appeared that scientific ingenuity had brought forth a monster, begotten by military necessity and nursed by political expediency. A generation which had already suffered two world wars regarded the monster's father and nurse with a certain amount of suspicion but, as usual, the mother got the blame.

Never has a scientific achievement been given a worse start in the sphere of human affairs than the release of atomic energy. The holocausts of Hiroshima and Nagasaki completely outshone half a century of patient and systematic scientific work into which the thought of death and destruction had never entered. The man in the street only beholds the spectre of a secret weapon, capable of obliterating a whole town in the fraction of a second. He does not realise that the problem of atomic energy had been freely discussed for decades past by scientists of all nations, and that the discovery of the process of nuclear fission which is utilized in the atomic bomb has been openly described in scientific journals for everyone to share.

To redress the balance between vague uneasiness and scientific truth is the foremost aim of this book. It is an attempt to translate the achievements of atomic research, culminating in the release of energy, from the language of the scientist into that of the average citizen. To give in a short book even a rough survey of the present-day knowledge of atomic structure and of the physical processes involved in the release of atomic energy is an ambitious task. Neither the intricacies of nuclear research nor the organisation of the development of the atomic bomb enter the scope of this narrative. Many excellent books have been written on the instruments and machines used by the atomic physicist and on the results obtained with them, while the part played by individual scientists or research groups in the production of the bomb has been described in the official statements by the British, Canadian and U.S. governments. Rather than dealing with technical problems, the task of the present book is to give a broad outline of the problems of nuclear energy from the viewpoint of the physicist.

The book is based to a great extent on two series of lectures, dealing with the principles of modern physics, which the author has given to lay audiences under the auspices of the Oxford University Delegacy for Extra-mural Studies. The chapters on the atomic bomb and the controlled release of atomic energy are based on accounts published in the scientific literature and on the official government statements. The book was originally planned in collaboration with Dr. J. G. Daunt who wrote the first drafts for chapters 3 and 7. While for technical reasons Dr. Daunt was unable to continue his work on the book, he has been kind enough to help in the revision of the manuscript and I am grateful to him for many helpful suggestions.

K. M.

CONTENTS

LIST OF PLATES

These Plates will be found following
page 64.

ACKNOWLEDGMENTS

The Author's acknowledgments are due to the following firms and individuals for permission to reproduce photographs in the Plates in this book :—

Edward H. Gooch Ltd. for the photographs on Plates I and II of Pierre Curie, Marie Curie and Henri Becquerel ; Elliott & Fry Ltd. for photographs of Lord Rutherford, Sir James Chadwick, Sir George Thomson and F. W. Aston on Plate I ; *New York Times Photos* for the photograph of Niels Bohr on Plate I, and for the Hanford Plutonium Plant on Plate III ; Sport & General for the photograph of Albert Einstein on Plate I ; Associated Press for the photograph of Enrico Fermi on Plate I, and the Trial explosion of the under-water atom bomb at Bikini on Plate X ; Central Press Photographs for the photograph of Frederick Jolliot on Plate I, and the photograph on Plate XI ; Madame Eve Curie and Messrs. William Heinemann for the photograph of the Curie Laboratory on Plate II ; The Information Office of the Canadian Government for the Separation of Pitchblende photograph on Plate III ; L.N.A., London, for the photograph of the Separation Plant at Clinton on Plate III ; Paul Karlson and Messrs. George Allen & Unwin Ltd. for photographs on Plate IV, and Plate VI, taken from his book "You and the Universe" ; Professor Chadwick for the photograph of Cloud Chamber Tracks on Plate V ; Drs. C. Moller and E. Rasmussen and Messrs. George Allen & Unwin Ltd. for photographs on Plate V, Plate VI, Plate VII and Plate IX, taken from their book "The World and the Atom" ; Dr. Powell of Bristol University for the Proton track photograph on Plate V ; Professors Dee and Walton and the Royal Society for the photograph of Lithium Bombardment on Plate VII ; Cambridge University Press for the photograph of Cockcroft & Walton's High Voltage Installation on Plate VIII ; International General Electric Co. of New York for the photograph of the Betatron on Plate VIII ; London Electrotype Agency for the two photographs of the Atom trial in the New Mexican Desert on Plate X ; Dr. J. G. Wilson of Manchester University for the photograph of the Mason Track on Plate VI ; Prof. Blackett and the Royal Society for a photograph on Plate VII.

Special thanks are due to Mr. William E. Dick, Editor of "Discovery," for a photograph on Plate IX, and for great assistance given in the unearthing of difficult material

Symbols used in this book:

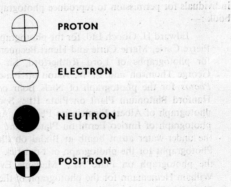

PROTON

ELECTRON

NEUTRON

POSITRON

CHAPTER ONE

THE ATOM

SINCE the dawn of history man's mind has contemplated the variety of materials which surround him and which have played an ever increasing part in his daily life. Until the advent of man, life on earth utilized the wealth of its environment only instinctively, to breathe, to eat and to drink; but, when some hundred thousand years ago our ancestors appeared, materials assumed a new meaning for them. While they could not eat stone or wood they began to realise the uses of stone and wood and of other materials as tools and weapons and to provide shelter. Man also acquired the mastery of fire and the evidence left by him in caves suggests that he turned these achievments to immediate account, using the weapons to kill his fellow man and the fire to cook him.

All the time his brain turned over the many problems that lay around him. What makes wood different from stone, and why does wood change to smoke and ashes, and stone not? These were some of the many questions which tortured him, the explanation of which he craved; for man cannot go on thinking unless he can put his thoughts into an orderly system.

When the twilight of the dim past changed to the bright day of history and written record, we find that the Greek philosopher Democritus (400 B.C.) taught a doctrine that is borne out remarkably well by the researches of modern science. Democritus postulated that whereas some kinds of matter change when heated or dissolved, there exist certain constituents, called elements, which always remain unchanged and which in various combinations form all the different things which surround us. He also stated that the elements differ from each other because they are made up of different kinds of building bricks. These bricks he called *atoms*, meaning indivisible units.

From the accumulation of knowledge that has been amassed in the many centuries since his time, it is evident today that Democritus was almost right. We know now that there are no less than 92 different kinds of atoms from which all things, including ourselves, are made. To take some examples which are most common in everyday life, consider the substance salt. This is composed of a combination of the elements sodium and chlorine. Water is a compound of the elements hydrogen and oxygen; glass mostly consists of oxygen and silicon bound together in tight chemical embrace. The individual particles of such substances are compound units made up of two or more atoms linked together in close proximity. They are called *molecules*. In this way by joining up different varieties of the 92 elements to form molecules, the almost infinite multitude of chemical materials can be made. They are all found to be composed of the comparatively small number of 92 apparently indivisible atoms. This is the basis of chemistry, the groundwork of our knowledge of substances.

During the last 50 years or so it has been found that such a simple scheme as the one proposed by Democritus, and retained by us for so long, is not enough. Atoms themselves despite their name are no longer the indivisible units they were once supposed to be. They are in themselves exceedingly complex structures, composed of still smaller and more fundamental units.

Complex as the structure of the atom appears to be, infinitely more complex than scientists believed a century ago, its composition is simple. This welcome find, this simplicity of make up, makes the whole picture much easier to describe and understand. Instead of having to imagine no less than 92 different particles each with its own attributes, it is now only necessary to indulge in three—the electron, the proton, and the neutron—these are the names of the three types of brick which together make the universe. Different combinations of these three " elementary particles " form all the 92 elements. It would be far beyond the scope of this book to attempt to cover the years of research, the patient thought and careful experiment that has gone to gain this knowledge. Each advance in thought and in technique has resulted in a greater clarity of our general view but at the same time has increased the complication of detail which a close scrutiny reveals. Let us stand back and regard the general picture that science today presents, looking only at those details which will help to further our line of thought.

The way in which nature's elementary particles are arranged in the atomic world provides the clue to all the mysterious changes which matter undergoes continually before our eyes, often at our own bidding. The melting of a snowflake, the burning of coal and the explosion of the atomic bomb are all rearrangements of the pattern formed by electrons, protons and neutrons. Investigation of this pattern more than any other problem has been the life work of scientists all the world over, and there is much that we know today. Still more, however, remains hidden from our eyes. The glare of the atomic bomb is a herald, announcing that the door has been prized open which leads to the very centre of the atom, where the final details in the structure of matter are to be found.

It is well known that atoms are extremely small. For example there are more than a million million million of them in a grain of fine table salt, and each of these atoms contains in itself about 50 elementary particles. To specify their *size* in the same kind of manner that is usually adopted in measuring the size of billiard balls or even of the earth is, however, a futile and misleading task. The ordinary man's conception of the size of a body is bound up with the fact that it occupies a certain amount of space and that this space therefore cannot be taken up at the same time by another body. The elementary particles of which an atom is composed, however, do not observe these simple rules: they are not like billiard balls shrunken to infinitely minute size. They are quite different and beyond our imaginative powers of model making. Their size is determined by the limits to which they can approach one another and these limits depend on the forces that the particles exert.

Although the size of a particle is a difficult question to decide, its weight and electric properties present far fewer difficulties. The weight of a proton, for example, is so very small that the number of them making up the weight of one ounce would be a figure with 24 noughts after it. For such a tiny weight as this clearly the ounce is too big a unit to employ. For measurements in the atomic world a new and more convenient unit has grown up. The unit is the proton itself. The weight of one proton is taken to be 1. On this new scale the weights of atoms become easy to grasp and memorise. But this is not all. The proton is used again to provide a unit of electric charge. Electricity is so intimately bound up with matter that the elementary particles themselves are mainly distinguished by whether and in what amount they bear electric charge. The electric charge of a proton is positive and its amount is defined as one unit. The proton therefore, one of the fundamental particles in the atom, has the weight 1 and electric charge + 1.

Of the other fundamental particles the neutron has a weight of 1, like the proton. But it has *no* electric charge. It is electrically neutral, hence its name. The electron has still smaller mass, weighing 1840 times less than a proton: but it has electric charge, negative in sign, equal in amount to that of the proton. Its charge is -1.

THE ELEMENTARY PARTICLES

Name	Weight	Electric Charge
Proton	1	+1
Neutron	1	0
Electron	1/1840	−1

With the electric charges and weights of the elementary particles satisfactorily defined, the process of atom building can begin. A great deal has been written in the past two decades concerning the structure of the atom, and pictures of atoms looking like miniature solar systems, with a sun and planets, are only too common. The atom, however, has never been seen with the naked eye nor with any of the elaborate instruments that science can command. Such pictures of the atom, describing it as a solar system or in similar ways, are therefore only models, mechanical models, which in so far as they are helpful are well and good. But it must never be forgotten that the atom itself is not mechanical in structure like engines or roundabouts. We shall find that the forces holding the atom together are very different from those between the sun and the earth and do not observe the same laws of action. Provided this is borne well in mind, such model-making need not lead us far astray.

The general pattern in which protons, neutrons and electrons are arranged is the same in every atom. There is an outer region populated entirely by electrons which sail continuously around a hard central core beneath, enveloping it like a cloud. The core inside is called the "nucleus." This nucleus, a tiny central lump of matter, is composed of protons and neutrons bound together in a tight compact mass. The conception of a nucleus with its encircling electrons was originally proposed as an atomic model by Rutherford and the great Danish physicist, Niels Bohr. This model is much like that of the sun with its planets round it, but with this first exception, that the masses bear electric charge. The central piece, the nucleus, having protons and neutrons only in its make up is positively charged, whereas the cloud of electrons round it is negatively charged.

One of the salient features of a complete atom taken by itself is that it appears to have no charge. Left undisturbed it is electrically neutral. Its make up, however, abounds in electric charges of both positive and negative variety. It is clear, therefore, that a complete atom must possess as many negative as positive unit charges in its construction, so that their effects outside the atom exactly cancel out. This great and important fact provides at once more detail in the picture of the nucleus and its enveloping electronic cloud. It demands that there must be as many positive protons in the nucleus as there are negatively charged electrons whirling round it. How many there are, depends on which of the 92 different atoms they make up.

The first and simplest atom has one electron circling round the nucleus. To balance out the electron's negative charge the nucleus consists of one proton of charge $+1$, and nothing more. This simple atom is the element hydrogen. The next atom on the list, the element helium, has two elec-

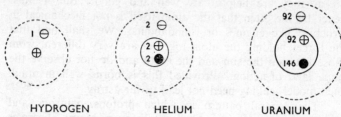

HYDROGEN   HELIUM   URANIUM
(number 1; weight 1)   (number 2; weight 4)   (number 92; weight 238)

Fig. 1. *This diagram shows how atoms are built up. There is a central nucleus made up of protons and neutrons which is enveloped in a " cloud " of electrons. The relative sizes of nucleus and electron cloud are not to scale.*

trons in its outer cloud. Its nucleus must contain, therefore, two protons with a charge $+2$. Here however comes the difficulty. Two protons each with a similar electric charge repel one another far too violently to stay cooped up in the small volume of the nucleus: without some kind of atomic mortar they would fly asunder. This is the role the neutrons play. Somehow, as will be discussed below at greater length, the addition of neutrons to the nuclear mass binds protons and neutrons all together in close proximity. To obtain a nucleus with a charge $+2$, not only two protons but also two neutrons are required. The helium nucleus therefore possesses the charge $+2$ and the weight 4.

The whole series of atoms from hydrogen with one electron in its outer cloud to uranium with 92 is built up step by step in this manner. Lithium, the third on the list, has three electrons in its outer cloud: beryllium has four: boron five, and so they go on. The number of electrons any atom holds is called its " atomic number." At each step up the nucleus possesses one more positive proton, and in order to balance out its electric charge, so that the atom as a whole shall be electrically neutral, one more electron has to be added to the cloud. The number of protons in the nucleus, therefore, determines the atomic number of the element. The number of neutrons on the other hand which the nucleus contains is not so easily stated. It can be said with certainty, however, that, with the exception of hydrogen, which being at the start of the series is in a somewhat unusual position, a nucleus must contain at least *as many* neutrons as protons in it to keep the assembly held together. Thus helium has 2 protons and 2 neutrons, lithium 3 and 4 and beryllium 4 and 5 respectively. At the end of the series comes uranium with 92 protons and 146 neutrons in its central core, giving it a total weight of 238. The sum of the number of protons and the number of neutrons in a nucleus, added up, gives its atomic weight.

With this model of the structure of atoms, made up from their three kinds of fundamental component particles, the question of their weight and size can be considered in a more comprehensive way. Consider for example an atom of oxygen, of atomic number 8. Its nucleus contains 8 protons and 8 neutrons: therefore its weight is 16 units, whereas that of all 8 electrons put together only comes to about 1/250 atomic units, only one part in 4000 of the total weight. Thus nearly all the weight resides in a tiny space right at the centre of the system, whose size is very much smaller than the whole atom appears to be.

Unlike the solar system whose planets revolve round the sun in one single plane, the atom has electrons moving around the nucleus in all directions, completely enveloping it as they do. If two atoms approach each other, it is these clouds of electrons shielding each nucleus, and not the nuclei themselves, that come together first. As they approach, the negatively charged clouds repel one another more and more violently the nearer they become. Electrical structures such as these cannot " touch " each other. Their sizes are given only by how closely they can approach against the forces of electric repulsion acting between them. Indeed it might appear from this point of view an impossible task to hold atoms together to form a solid body. However, as we shall see later, there are yet other forces at work tending to draw neighbour atoms in together. A collection of atoms therefore will take up positions in which the forces pulling them together are just balanced out by the mutual repulsions of their electronic clouds. This balance of forces thus decides the size of things. To compress atoms together or to pull them apart beyond this balance point, these forces must be overcome and energy used up in doing so. Here for the first time we see how atoms and energy are linked closely together, a fact of so much importance in the question of atomic energy.

The picture of the complete atom as it now stands before us can be divided into two aspects, that presented by the nucleus and that of the electron cloud. These two aspects, though distinct, are not independent since in a neutral atom the number of electrons must always be the same as that of the protons in the nucleus. It should be emphasized, however, that it is the composition of the nucleus which determines the electron cloud and not vice versa. If, for instance a proton, i.e. a unit positive charge, is taken out of a nucleus, the electron cloud must immediately loose one of its electrons Conversely, if a nucleus is enriched by one proton, one more electron will be added to the cloud. On the earth such changes in the composition of atomic nuclei are very rare events and there is always a sufficient number of unattached electrons floating about from which a deficiency in the electron cloud can be made up. On the other hand the nucleus will remain quite unchanged if one or two electrons are taken away from an atom even when provision is made at the same time for the atom not to pick up any stray electrons. In this case the atom will have an excess positive charge and if it continues its existence it is called a positive "ion." Its lack of outer electrons will, however, make no difference whatsoever to the composition of the nucleus.

Thus it is the nucleus which ultimately determines the character of the atom and if one chemical element shall be "transmuted" into another, the *nuclei* of its atoms must be altered. The change undergone by uranium atoms in the explosion of the atomic bomb is a change in the nucleus. and it would indeed have been a happier choice of terms if the bomb had been called "nuclear" rather than "atomic." While our account must concern itself mainly with the problems of the nucleus, frequent reference will have to be made to the structure and peculiarities of the outer electrons of the atom.

So far the assembly of electrons which envelop the

nucleus has been referred to vaguely as a cloud but in reality this cloud is built up according to a definite pattern. The significant feature of this pattern is its subdivision into a number of layers or " shells " as they are usually called.

Starting again with the hydrogen atom and proceeding to higher atomic numbers, the first irregularity is encountered in element number 3, lithium. This atom has a nuclear charge of +3 and must therefore have 3 electrons. The preceding atom, helium (number 2) has 2 electrons sailing around the nucleus at equal distances but it is found that the forces of repulsion of these two electrons will not allow a third one to be placed among them. To form a lithium atom therefore the third electron which must be added has to rotate alone at a greater distance from the nucleus than the other

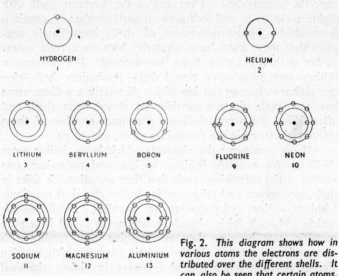

HYDROGEN
1

HELIUM
2

LITHIUM
3

BERYLLIUM
4

BORON
5

FLUORINE
9

NEON
10

SODIUM
11

MAGNESIUM
12

ALUMINIUM
13

Fig. 2. *This diagram shows how in various atoms the electrons are distributed over the different shells. It can also be seen that certain atoms, for example Lithium and Sodium, are similar in the arrangement of the outermost electrons. The circles are meant to signify the different electron shells and do not represent the orbits of rotation. The number below the name of the element is the atomic number.* (See Appendix 1, 2)

two. The following seven electrons which are successively added to form the atoms of beryllium, boron, carbon, nitrogen, oxygen, fluorine and neon will all keep company with the initially solitary third lithium electron. But at the next step, the formation of sodium, the eight electrons at this layer which form the outer crust of the neon atom allow no further room for a newcomer and the necessary extra electron has to exist further out from the centre and start a new layer there. Thus electron shells are formed which, when they are fully occupied, do not admit further electrons.

It requires little imagination to see that the further one goes away from the nucleus the more spacious will the electron shells grow. The innermost, the helium shell, holds only two electrons. The next one, the neon shell, holds eight, and the same number can be placed into the following one, the argon shell· Then comes the krypton shell with eighteen electrons, and so it goes on until number 92, uranium is reached. This arrangement of shells immediately suggests that there must be a similarity between certain atoms as far as their external shape is concerned. For instance, a lithium atom possesses a closed shell—the helium shell—plus one solitary electron outside of it. Similarly a sodium atom has one single electron outside the closed neon shell, and after filling the argon shell we encounter another of these solitary electrons in the potassium atom, and so on.

If one compares the elements which have similar outer shells, as for example lithium, sodium and potassium, one arrives at the surprising result that they are all much alike in their appearance and take part in similar chemical reactions. Lithium, sodium and potassium are so-called " alkali " metals which, although fairly abundant, are never found in a pure metallic state because they all combine most readily with many other elements. There are other atoms which are also similar to each other and also engage in violent chemical reactions. They are fluorine, chlorine, bromine and iodine which all possess complete outer shells except for one missing electron. Helium, neon argon and krypton on the other hand, whose atoms have completed shells with no electrons either extra to them or missing, are all inert gases and form no chemical compounds at all.

röntgenum.

NEON SHELL

HELIUM SHELL

ARGON SHELL

KRYPTON SHELL

Fig. 3. *Electron shells. There are two more shells possible, the Xenon shell and the Radon shell. The latter is uncompleted when the series of elements breaks off with Uranium (No. 92). (See Appendix 2).*

This astounding similarity between certain chemical elements had in fact been discovered long before scientists had any idea of atomic structure. In 1869 the Russian chemist Mendeleëff grouped the then known elements according to their chemical properties and similarities in what has become known as the " periodic table " (see appendix) but the reason for the similarities remained obscure. Only the advent of atomic research threw light on this mystery by showing that Mendeleëff's groups correspond to the different electron shells. The arrangement of the shells explains not only the chemical characteristics of the elements but also certain of their physical properties. However, the enumeration of all the connections between the arrangement of the outer electrons and the physical or chemical properties of the elements lies well outside the scope of this book. The amount of scientific research that has been devoted to this subject and the amount of detailed information gathered is stupendous. For us it will suffice to realise that the appearance and chemical behaviour of matter is the property of the *outermost* layers of electrons in the atom. Iron, gold and sulphur present to us different aspects because the numbers of electrons in the outermost layer of their respective atoms are different.

A chemical reaction between elements, as for instance the combination of iron and oxygen to form rust, is caused by a rearrangement of the electrons in this outer layer. This is a revelation of fundamental importance, because it shows that even with the most drastic chemical methods of attack it is never possible to do more than scrape the fringes of an atom's electron cloud. The sources from which the atomic bomb derives its power are on the other hand the hidden forces which are locked up within the nucleus· To engage them we cannot rely on the test tube and the crucible of chemical research. Other more powerful agents than acids and fire have to be found before the fortress of the atomic nucleus can be attacked.

Finally we must return to the way atoms and nuclei are built up in order to settle one last important point, the question why the sum total of atoms of different kinds should be the somewhat undistinguished number 92. The last atom, number 92, is uranium, an element similar to the rare earths metals. Chemically there is no reason why this should be the end. As far as the structure of the electronic cloud is concerned, atom building could continue beyond uranium. The trouble does not lie here at all: we could probably go on building bigger and better atoms indefinitely if nuclei could be made with high enough electric charges. Something however has been going wrong in that department even before the number 92 is reached. Beginning with the number 84, atomic nuclei become more and more difficult to manage. They hold together for some time but then break up again rather like an oversized cathedral built of toy bricks. When they break up they do not just collapse: they explode with a force many thousand times stronger than that produced by T.N.T. Two of these last atoms, numbers 85 and 87, are so

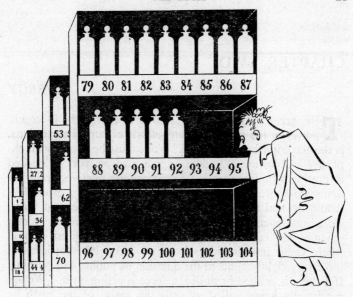

Fig. 4. WHY ARE THERE ONLY 92 ELEMENTS?

unstable that they have not yet been found. Of the others there is a famous member. It is radium, number 88.

The process of atom construction must have once taken place when the world was born into the shape in which we see it today and it is still going on to some extent inside stars and in the depths of the universe. From the universe at large messages reach us day by day in the form of rays more powerful than we have known in laboratory experiments, telling us of atoms being created and destroyed. The building up of new and so far unknown atoms in the laboratory was first attempted about 10 years ago and it was in these experiments that scientists stumbled upon the process of the release of atomic energy.

CHAPTER TWO

ENERGY

THE great purpose of any source of energy, be it atomic power or the relatively puny efforts of our own exertions, is the accomplishment of work. Work must be done by an explosive in blowing a building down, just as work is needed in putting a building up. To compare the relative merits for doing work of an atomic bomb and T.N.T. or for example a steamship and a horse and cart, our natural ideas of force, work and energy must be put into some kind of orderly scheme that can be used. Scientific method must step in where vague intuitive ideas leave off. Our inherent ideas of force very rightly concern the question of pulling and pushing. If a thing is pushed or pulled, a force is acting on it. We are continually being pulled towards the centre of the earth by the force of gravity and two pith balls, both bearing a positive electric charge, are pushed apart by electric force.

However great the force of gravity may be, if we do not move no work is done. Work is expended only when force is overcome and objects are moved against the action of the force. For example, if a man climbs a flight of stairs, he does work against the force of gravity. The work done can alternatively be called an " energy." His energy is higher as the result of the process of climbing up the stairs to the fifth floor than it was at the street level. That he has gained energy by doing work in this way, he could easily find out by experiment. By letting himself down on a pulley he could draw up a load of bricks on the other side. By parting thus with his energy, it is converted into work again in lifting up the bricks.

Energy can be stored and used in many ways. Mechanical methods are not the only ones· Mechanical work can be used to produce heat. Energy is expended in rubbing two sticks together and heat results, as our ancestors found before matches were invented. Energy is used up in turning a

22

Fig. 5. *VARIOUS WAYS OF DOING WORK*

dynamo and it appears instead in the form of electricity. In what ever way energy is stored or used, this fact emerges, namely a thing contains energy if it is capable of doing work. A compressed spring, an electric battery and even a piece of coal contain energy which when released can shoot a bolt or drive a motor or work an engine. Moreover energy cannot be destroyed. In some of its forms it is easily apparent, whereas in others it is hidden: but this fact does not affect its nature, rather it is due to the limits of our perception and our experience. We learn in early childhood that a flying stone contains energy, but to perceive that a compressed spring also has energy comes at a later date. Even those who know all about compressed springs may innocently use a stick of dynamite as an emergency tent peg unless the object is well labelled.

To measure energy, the amount of work which it can do must be measured. Measurements of this kind can always be done in a variety of ways. For example, in measuring

Fig. 6. ENERGY OF MOTION AND HIDDEN ENERGY

the length of this line of print, use can be made of inches, a unit derived from the length of the human foot, or in centimetres, a unit derived from the circumference of the earth. In measuring work, one unit that can be used is the work done in lifting the weight of one pound up through one foot: alternatively it could be measured as the work required to heat a gallon of water through one degree. Different as these units appear to be, they are both measures of the same thing, energy. In the present age, when electrical energy is so important in daily life, a new electric measure of energy has grown up, namely the kilowatt-hour. As we pay for the use of our light, our electric fires and many other things by the kilowatt-hour, and as this must have conveyed an idea of the value of such energy, the kilowatt-hour will serve as a most convenient unit of energy in this book. The picture on page 25 shows what a kilowatt-hour can do.

With these concrete ideas of energy in mind we can tackle afresh the problem of atomic energy with better prospects. The atomic model so far developed, consisting of a

Fig. 7. WHAT ONE KILOWATT-HOUR CAN DO

Fire 10 anti-aircraft shells   *Warm your back for 2 hours*

Drive your car 5 miles   *Bring 65 kettles to the boil*

small tightly packed nucleus surrounded by a comparatively vast and tenuous cloud of electrons, is in striking contrast to the solid tangible appearance of, for instance, a piece of iron or a stone. Much has been made of the surprising revelation that matter in the main consists of empty space. Its great emptiness is forcefully brought home if it is realised that the nucleus in an atom of iron is as small as a pea placed at the centre of a space as large as Piccadilly Circus. This is a fact that most men frankly disbelieve, and they can hardly be blamed for doing so. Indeed their incredulity is in some ways justified, for in stretching a model of the atom to such a size it becomes inadequate. Although the mass of the atom is indeed extremely thinly distributed throughout its volume, the spaces in between cannot by any stretch of the imagination be considered empty. They are full of energy to an almost unbelievable extent. A pea in the centre of Piccadilly Circus appears so small and lonely because the forces which it can exert on us are quite negligible. The force of gravity which is the only one we should naturally consider in these circumstances is for a pea far too small to be impressive. How much smaller would the forces between two peas appear, one situated in Piccadilly Circus and the other in Trafalgar Square. Yet such a picture would, on the simple planetary model of the atom, describe the arrangement of two neighbour nuclei each situated in its own electronic cloud: and on the atomic scale the forces between them would be sufficient to account for the strength of a piece of granite. Pictures of peas distributed over the map of London can give no clue to the strength of these atomic attractive forces. The answer lies in the hidden energy of the atom. Inside and around an atom forces are acting which are many thousand times stronger than the force of gravity. These forces account for the cohesion of matter and provide a great well of hidden energy.

The great fund of energy hidden in cohesive forces can be gauged in a rough way by the energy required to break a stick or crack a lump of ice. In doing this the forces between neighbour atoms are overcome. A more accurate measure can be made by melting the substance under test, for in destroying its rigidity in this way the forces linking each atom with its neighbours are overcome throughout the material as a whole. The energy needed to melt a pound of ice amounts to .04 kilowatt-hours, enough to lift a motor car from the ground up onto the roof of a house. It should be clear now why matter can appear so rigid. The nuclei of matter in an armour plate are as sparcely placed as a collection of apples separated from each other by a distance of about three miles, and yet to us it appears impenetrable· The barrier in our path is not the apples, but the strong forces binding them and their surrounding electron clouds together.

In the process of melting not even the outer fringes of atoms are disturbed. Water and ice retain their chemical identity. The outermost layer of the electron cloud of each atom remains unchanged. Only a separation of atom from atom and molecule from molecule has been effected. To effect a rearrangement of electrons much larger energies are required, and such rearrangements result, as we have seen, in a change of chemical identity.

A spectacular chemical change occurs in the formation of water molecules from their constituent atoms of hydrogen and oxygen. Two parts of hydrogen are required for every one of oxygen, and a spark must be sent through the gaseous mixture to "trigger off" the reaction.. The spectacular nature of this reaction, as the author found in his schoolboy

Fig. 8. *ENERGY RESERVOIRS " TRIGGERED OFF "*

days, is its explosive speed. Hazardous as it may be in experiment, in theory it is a simple change. In combining together to form water molecules, the electronic etructure of
the hydrogen and oxygen atoms is rearranged. In water two
electrons in the outermost layer of the oxygen's electron
cloud are shared with two hydrogen atoms, binding them
together in molecular bondage. This new arrangement has
smaller energy than the first one, just as a man on the street
level has lower energy than when at the fifth floor. Moreover by letting himself down from the fifth floor a man could
pull up a load of bricks, thus giving off energy and so similarly the oxygen and hydrogen atoms descend to a lower
" energy level " when forming water; and energy is at the
same time given off. Of course the same amount of energy
must be put back into the water if it is required to split it up
again into hydrogen and oxygen gas.

The energy liberated when a pound of water is formed
in this way is approximately 2 kilowatt-hours, 50 times larger
than the energy needed to melt a pound of ice. Rearranging
electrons on the surface of the atoms of a single pound of
water requires as much work as raising 50 cars onto the roof
of a house. It is this energy, derived from the very skin of
atoms, that supplies the power for our factories, ships
and railways. The burning of a lump of coal is a rearrangement of this kind, whereby a carbon atom is made to share
four electrons of its outer layer with two atoms of oxygen
with which it is combined· This change produces about 4
kilowatt-hours per pound of coal.

In both these reactions the energy is in some way
locked in. We can keep a lump of coal in contact with the
air indefinitely but the chemical combination of carbon and
oxygen does not take place unless the coal is heated first.
Similarly hydrogen and oxygen gas have to be ignited with ι
spark before they explode to form water. Once the reaction
is " triggered off," it goes on by itself. Other reactions, as
for example the rusting of a nail, do not require such a fuse
to get them going. This unlocking of the energy store is a
characteristic feature of power producing chemical changes,
other examples being the ignition of petrol vapour and of
dynamite. The same phenomenon occurs again in the re-

lease of atomic power, where, too, a key is being used to unlock the energy of the uranium nucleus in the atomic bomb.

The existence or rather the creation of such carefully locked power reservoirs is the fundament on which our modern technical world is based. The machine age relies on huge man-made energy stores which can be opened and closed at our bidding and which are replenished from energy sources that are distant or only available occasionally. Coal which represents latent solar energy that has been stored by the plants of bygone geological periods, is brought from the depths of the earth and placed into contact with the oxygen of the air. The two partners in the power producing reaction, carbon atoms and oxygen molecules, are thus brought together in great quantity by the effort of man. A coal cellar or a petrol tank, provided they are filled, are energy stores from which we can draw a supply of power whenever we want to do so. To build up these reservoirs, work has to be expended, but the amount of energy spent in mining coal or in drilling for and refining petrol is less than the energy that coal and petrol provide when the chemical reactions in which they take part are triggered off.

The purposeful accumulation of energy stores is not a human invention. A plant gathers solar energy and uses it to build up chemical energy stores in its tissues and animals eat the energy stores provided by plants, transforming them by a complicated mechanism into still more convenient reservoirs from which energy in great quantity can be released at will. Thus animals, fundamentally parasites in nature's botanical gardens, are capable of sudden and violent action, of attack and defence. The central nervous system and the brain, organs which are not needed by the plant, act as control stations in the power house of the body. This peculiar faculty of hoarding, storing and releasing of energy is one of the striking manifestations of " life " and is possibly the basic phenomenon by which its mechanism is distinguished from the energy changes of inanimate matter. By mining coal, drilling for petrol and lastly tapping the energy reserve of atomic nuclei, man unconsciously follows a line of development which was initiated millions of years ago when the first organisms appeared on the face of the globe. The progressive stages of this development now stand clearly before us. The plant, essentially a primitive organism, catches the energy bearing rays of the sun whenever they come its way. Perhaps its earliest ancestor only just managed to store precariously the solar energy provided in a day in order to survive the following night. The energy storage mechanism of the plant, which enables it to build itself up from inorganic matter and from the energy provided by the sun, seems to impose its own limitation on the possible development of the organism. The primitive plant's modern descendents, the trees and shrubs in our garden are certainly impressive in comparison with the single cell of a bacterium. Their leafs are cleverly fanned out to gather the maximum energy, but no one can deny that they are less developed organisms than a man, a frog or a flea. Animals depend on plants to prepare their foods, that is to utilize energy and minerals and to bring them into a suitable form for the animal to devour. Not only does the animal make use of the energy provided in the tissues of plants and in the free oxygen exhaled by the plant, but also a new form of energy hoarding is developed. Contrary to the habit of the plant the animal does not wait patiently until energy comes along, but it goes about, seeking out the best and most easily accessible energy sources. In man the instinctive processes of food gathering and of protecting the energy storing mechanism of the body was put on a new level. The place of instinctive actions was taken by thought and considered foresight. By gathering firewood and by developing agriculture and husbandry, man created chemical energy stores outside his body. The use of domestic animals for ploughing, drawing water and as a means of transport constituted a further step, namely the controlled release of *mechanical* energy from the stores of chemical power in them.

This short digression into the domain of biology will have shown that our tendency to gather and store energy for the purpose of controlled release is a phenomen which is intimately bound up with the processes of life. On the other hand, the physical processes going on in the world at large, in which living organisms play no essential part, do not seem to favour this accumulation of energy that is so assiduously pursued by the atoms in the structure of living matter. On the contrary, any accumulation of energy which in the course of inorganic evolution in the universe has come into a form from which it can easily be released, will be triggered off sooner or later. As we shall see, new stars which suddenly flare up in the sky seem to bear witness to such "accidentally" released explosions. It is therefore not surprising that by the time man appeared on earth there were hardly any energy stores left for him to trigger off. Only dry grass of one season's growth or perhaps a few dead branches and even these had to be collected. From the beginning, man has had to put in work in order to create his energy reservoirs, and today the tapping of atomic energy is no exception to this rule. In the case of the atomic bomb man has to gather painstakingly the correct type of atom before some of the energy vested in the nuclei can be let loose. This is a fairly satisfactory state of affairs because it gives us a certain, though not an absolute, safeguard against the possibility that one day "sorcerer's apprentices" in some laboratory will set off the whole globe and thereby thoroughly defeat their own aim of hoarding energy.

Energy stores which can be controlled or triggered off need not be of chemical or nuclear nature. In fact an important and beautifully clear example is furnished by the utilization of water power. In the ordinary course of events water, evaporated by radiation from the sun off the ocean surfaces, falls as rain or snow in the elevated regions of the globe and returns in rivers to the level of the sea. The volume of water varies much with the season and man's primitive contrivances, little water wheels which tried to extract some of the energy of motion, were ill-suited to the conditions of changing flow. In order not to waste the energy contained in spring floods, dams are built across narrow valleys to catch the annual gush of water in artificial lakes. These reservoirs containing large masses of water with a high "head" are, of course, huge stores of energy, since each pound of water dropping from the high to the low level can do work just as a man can in letting himself down from a five storeyed building. By opening and closing a number of sluice gates and feeding the water into turbo-generators which produce electric current, energy can be drawn from the reservoir at discretion.

The whole energy store can also be triggered off at once. This in fact was done most successfully in the war when bombers of the R.A.F. destroyed the Möhne dam which feeds part of the Ruhr industries. Once the dam was breached by bombs, the energy of motion of the water rushing out played havoc with the rest of the structure and in a few hours the energy which had been accumulated over the span of a year was dispersed. It is significant that the energy that was needed for the trigger action, namely the energy expended by the bombs, was insignificant in comparison with the energy released. The latter would have sufficed to keep a considerable section of the whole Ruhr industry going for a year.

The picture of a reservoir or a trough filled with water conveys an excellent model of energy accumulation. In such a trough hidden energy is stored. The measure of the store of energy locked in by the surrounding walls is given by the amount of water stored and the "head." The greater the difference in level between the surface of the water and the bottom of the trough where the water can be drawn off to do work the greater the hidden energy there is.

Such a picture as this of an "energy trough," in which the level at which the energy is stored is an all important feature, has a more general application far exceeding that of dams and hydro-electric plants. It has been used by physicists to describe all sorts of stores of hidden energy. It can be applied to the movement of the planets about the sun. The earth, for example, can be pictured as moving around the inside surface of a trough of energy created by the gravitational attraction between it and the sun. If by some miracle the earth were stopped suddenly in its orbit it would drop like a stone straight into the sun. In doing so it would part with the hidden energy it has due to its distance from the gravitating sun, just as a man in letting himself down from a five storeyed building gives up hidden energy. The further the earth might be from the sun, the greater would be the release of hidden energy when it fell towards

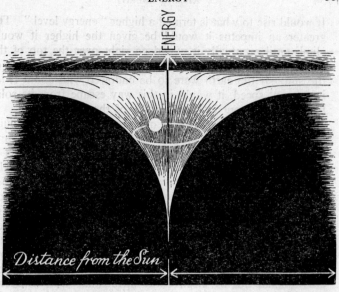

Fig. 9.   *The earth rotates in an imaginary " energy trough " which is created by the gravitational attraction of the sun.*

it.   Thus the distance between the earth and the sun gives a measure of the " height " of the level of hidden energy the earth possesses.

We can therefore draw a picture of a trough, the level at the bottom representing the fate of a planet which has lost all its hidden energy by being at the same place as the sun itself.   The earth in its present orbit would occupy a level— an energy level—some way up the side of the trough's walls; at which it is kept by the centrifugal force due to its own speed.   As it circles round the sun, we can picture it as moving round, always at the same level, the smooth inner surface of the energy trough, somewhat like a rider on the " wall of death."

If the earth by some strange chance were to be given extra energy and thereby to increase its speed, it would use this energy to move further away from the sun and so climb up the walls of the energy trough in which it is confined.

It would rise to what is termed a higher " energy level." The greater an impetus it would be given the higher it would climb until eventually it would go right over the top of the walls of the trough and out of the gravitational influence of the sun. If the earth were to be endowed with about twice its present speed, it would in this way escape from its solar trough and fly out into the depths of the universe.

To move the earth from one energy level in its trough to another and higher one, it must first be speeded up, and to speed it up it must be given energy. A jump upwards in energy level, therefore, needs energy put in to produce the jump, just as energy is needed to lift a stone from the floor to shoulder height. Conversely if the earth, or any body confined in an energy trough, goes from one energy level to a lower one, it must in the process release some of its hidden energy, in amount proportional to the difference it has fallen.

An electron, circling around the atomic nucleus, too, lives in an energy trough, produced in this case not by gravitational but by electrostatic attraction. But, while we cannot imagine a process by which the energy of the earth may be increased so that it would bid farewell to the sun, the energy of electrons can be raised easily in a number of ways, as for instance by heating. The re-arrangement of electrons in chemical processes must therefore acquire now a much deeper meaning. Clearly it is not the difference of arrangement in space which really matters but the level taken up by the electron in its energy trough. If, for instance, an electron in a chemical reaction is lifted from its trough over a barrier and drops into a lower trough, then the reaction will produce energy in the same way as energy is produced when water falls from one level to another. The energy level of the electron after the reaction is lower than it was before, and in the process of dropping to the new level the electron liberates energy, just as the man can in letting himself down from the fifth floor to the ground level.

Any analogy between the re-grouping of the electrons on the surface of an atom—such as occurs in a burning lump of coal—and the tremendous energy of a thundering express-train may appear far-fetched. In the same way imagination may boggle at the comparison of the exchange of electrons between different sets of atoms, or the drop of electrons from one energy level to another, with the explosive violence of a bursting bomb, and find the gulf too wide. Nevertheless, the gap can be bridged, and in a simple way. Just as the release of hidden energy in the stretched string of a bow makes an arrow fly away at speed, so the energy set free by rearrangement of electrons in a chemical reaction imparts a motion to the atoms taking part. Hidden energy is changed into energy of motion. Each atom or molecule concerned in the reaction starts off in aimless flight and will collide with its neighbours setting them, too, moving in an agitated career. These in their turn stir up more atoms and molecules lying in their path and so it goes on. When oxygen and hydrogen is fuzed together the speed imparted in this way to the water molecules produced is very great, and their violent movement appears to our senses as the intense heat and pressure of the explosion. If the vessel containing the hydrogen and oxygen is made of glass, the speed attained by the molecules is sufficient to sever the links which bind the vessel's molecules together, and the bottle bursts. If the same process is carried out with petrol vapour in the engine of a car, the hidden energy can be harnessed. In this way the exchange of outer electrons dropping from one " level " to another can take us on a week-end holiday.

This brief survey of the manifold ways in which energy can be changed into work, sometimes hiding away in atomic and sub-atomic places and at others bursting into view in a surge of power, lacks one more aspect to make the chart complete. Energy can take another and more elusive form, completely divorced from matter or its motion, namely the form of light. Everyone observing an explosion will notice that it does not only go off with a bang but also with a flash. The flash consists of light waves and they too carry some of the energy away. From a coal fire we receive energy from the combustion of coal not in the form of molecular bolts but in the form of radiation. Energy, thus, is not only transported by pieces of matter hurled out from the reaction but also by waves of light and heat. In this tenuous guise, great rivers and torrents of energy flow out from the sun and stars. Broadcasting stations pump out radio waves of energy over the whole surface of the earth, and the penetrating energy of X-rays is another form of the same phenomenon. All these means of transporting energy from place to place, in spite of the apparent differences they present, are identical in form. They are called quite generally " electro-magnetic waves," and only differ from each other in their length. Radio waves have gigantic length, ranging from ten to hundreds of metres long; whereas the wavelength of light is only about 1/50,000 inches. X-rays have wavelengths that are smaller still.

When the electrons in the outer layers of an atom are re-arranged in a chemical reaction, some of the energy released changes into a beam of light. In this connection there is one most important point in the relation between energy and radiation. The *greater* the energy of the change which takes place, the *shorter* is the wavelength of the rays that are sent out. It is well known that the hotter an explosion the more blue is the flash of light which accompanies it. This is because blue and violet light has a shorter wavelength than red, yellow or green light. It is not surprising therefore that one of the most powerful means of studying the structure and changes of structure within the atom lies in the analysis of the light which it emits. This is a great branch of physics, called spectroscopy, which provides a fund of information about the arrangement of electrons in the topmost layers of the atom's crust. By this means most of our knowledge of the outer fringes of the atom has been gleaned.

Supplementing this method of observing with light the way atoms are built up, there is another method of attack by which the atom can be probed to greater depths. This is by means of X-rays. With them the innermost layers of the electron cloud can be plumbed with ease and the details of their structure understood. The electro-magnetic waves that constitute X-rays have wavelengths as small as 1/500,000,000 inches, far smaller than those of light, and consequently they must be linked with energy changes within the atom far greater than those creating light. That their energy must be great is evident from the way they can penetrate huge thicknesses of matter. From the evidence that has been amassed in the 50 years since Roentgen first discovered them, it is known today that X-rays are due to disturbances and re-arrangements of electrons in the lower strata of the cloud around the atom.

One fact stands out from all these observations. The deeper we dig inside the atom, the greater are the energy changes that are involved. The explosion of T.N.T., impressive as it may appear, affects merely the topmost layer of the atom. It is a puny thing compared with the energy reserves buried deeper down below. The energy released in X-rays is, per atom, enormously much greater than that from dynamite. Unfortunately while we can produce changes in the lower levels of the electron cloud, these re-arrangements are only of a momentary nature. We have not found the means to store and release energy at will in this region of the atom and it appears unlikely that we shall ever be able to make use of them as a source of power by such means as are at our disposal in the laboratory.

However, before man had time to realise that a new " chemistry " of the lower strata of the electron cloud was not in his reach, a still brighter star arose on the horizon of scientific discovery, radioactivity. Hardly had scientists time to recover from their surprise about the tremendous energy of X-rays, than they had to realise that there are still more powerful rays in comparison with which those discovered by Roentgen are as paltry as light waves are in comparison with X-rays. This latest addition to the range of electro-magnetic waves, called gamma-rays, brought the first message of the existence of the atomic nucleus. This first faint glimpse of atomic nuclei shown in radioactivity, which was observed first by a French scientist in 1896, heralded the way to the terrifying catastrophies of Hiroshima and Nagasaki half a century later.

CHAPTER THREE

RADIOACTIVITY

THE up-to-date model of the atom, with an account of which we have begun our story is, of course, the outcome of a long trail of research and theory. The real story began just half a century ago in a Paris laboratory, and in spite of the impressive construction of modern atom-smashing plants and huge atomic bomb factories we are still very much at the beginning. Atomic physics, a new branch of science which has only grown up in our own life-time, has to-day become the most important aspect of our physical world and has transformed completely man's conception of the forces by which the universe keeps going.

The haphazard and secretive activities of the ancient alchemists, motivated chiefly by a desire for gain, found expression in a quest for power to transmute one element into another. Their goal was the philosopher's stone whereby gold could be formed from baser stuff, and, as we can see to-day, it was a goal that they could never have attained with the means at their disposal. The mere application of fire or the corrosive action of chemical attack which were the only weapons in their armoury can only affect the outer fringes of the atom and leave untouched the nucleus beneath. So convinced were true scientists of the immutability of atoms that by the end of the nineteenth century the pendulum had swung the other way. Transmutation of elements was considered an old wife's fable, akin to witchcraft, and the dogma of the permanency and indestructibility of the elements was the order of the day. The apparent stability of social man, accepted so widely in Victoria's reign, was reflected even in the realms of scientific thought. Matter to them could not be destroyed.

Such belief as there was in the changeless nature of the atomic world was rudely destroyed in 1896. From one experiment made by Henri Becquerel a revolution in physics began, a revolution as great as any in the social history of mankind, which, followed up, has led to the release of atomic power in our day.

At that time the whole scientific world was excited about X-rays, which had only just been discovered the year before, and the effects of these new rays were being studied everywhere. Very little was known about the way in which the new rays were generated and Becquerel had formed the idea that X-rays or a similar kind of radiation might be emitted by minerals which had been exposed to the light of the sun. In order to test his hypothesis he placed his specimens, after putting them out into the sunlight, on photographic plates. To his great astonishment he discovered, almost by accident, that certain minerals which had not been exposed to the sun would affect the plates in exactly the same way as X-rays. These minerals were salts of the element uranium. He concluded therefore that from uranium an invisible penetrating radiation went out, akin to that of X-rays, which was capable of penetrating thicknesses of matter opaque to visible light (plate II). In some way uranium was generating powerful rays. This new phenomenon was called " ratioactivity."

The radioactive properties of uranium, and of other elements besides, was soon found to be due to spontaneous changes going on within the atom. All attempts to affect the process by chemical reactions, by the application of heat or cold or by the most violent physical actions that could be used, made no difference at all to its radioactive powers. To-day we know that all these kinds of attacks, affecting as they do only the outer electronic cloud round each uranium nucleus, could make no impression on its newly discovered properties. Radioactivity must be, it was soon concluded, a spontaneous process occurring within the very centre of the atom, and going on and on inexorably until the active material is all used up. It was with this knowledge in mind that Marie and Pierre Curie started their search for unknown radioactive elements (plate II).

The dramatic nature of the Curies' work, brought so recently and so effectively to the public eye, has its parallel to-day in the production of the atomic bomb. In their search they started with a mountain of about five tons of of pitchblende, a mineral ore rich in uranium, and proceeded step by step to separate out the active from the inert parts, until in the end they were able to isolate about 1/300th of an ounce of the material they sought. During this arduous process it became evident much to their surprise that the radioactive elements only constituted a tiny fragment of the total weight of the stuff they started with. As with the process of separation of the type of atom required for the atomic bomb, out of tons and tons of crude ore the precious element is extracted only grain by grain. The most well known radioactive element which the Curie's obtained in this laborious way was radium, which because of its strong radio-action and other convenient properties is most widely known. It is not, however, by any means the only element which shows radioactive effects, as the Curies were themselves the first to show.

The first public reaction to the work of the Curies was incredulity. When it became clear that their staggering observations could not be doubted, utter amazement was followed by a flood of scientific speculations and questions. What was the process that made atoms disgorge energy? Why did it go on all the time and where did the energy come from? In spite of the most ingenious and tortuous attempts at explanation it became abundantly clear that in radioactivity physicists were faced with a new phenomenon for which there was no room in the accepted system of science.

Even before the full importance of radioactivity had been realised, doubts about the unchangeable nature of atoms had begun to arise. In 1897 J. J. Thomson had established the existence of the electron and showed that its mass was about 2,000 times smaller than that of the hydrogen atom. While there was as yet no evidence that electrons might actually form part of an atom, the existence of a particle of sub-atomic weight gave cause for suspicion. In 1902 Rutherford and Soddy took the decisive step which broke all traditional concepts of physics and chemistry and advanced the theory that radioactivity is caused by a spontaneous breaking-up of atoms. They had been led to this conclusion by studying the nature of the radiation which is emitted by the radioactive elements.

In the case of radium it was found that "alpha-particles" (plate V) were emitted and that these particles were in fact identical with the nuclei of atoms of helium. One by one the nuclei of radium explode, ejecting from their interior a helium nucleus in the process. Just as a stick of dynamite shoots out pieces of itself far and wide when it explodes, so radium nuclei throw off pieces of the stuff of which they are composed. But this is not all. Like the flash of light from dynamite, some of the energy of the exploding radium is carried away as "gamma rays," electro-magnetic waves like those of light, but many times more powerful. Such a cataclysmic event as this, being as if the earth in volcanic turmoil threw off a moon far into the depths of space, has a profound effect on what is left behind. No longer does the disintegrated atom of radium show the typical properties of radium, which is a metallic element similar to barium; but with the make-up of the nucleus changed it becomes a quite new element. By disintegration it is changed to "radon," which is not a metal but an inert gas similar in its chemical properties to other inert gases such as helium and neon.

This striking change from a metal into a gas caused the greatest surprise when it was first discovered but, from what has been said earlier about atomic structure, it is exactly the thing one would have to expect. When the helium nucleus, which itself consists of 2 neutrons and 2 protons, breaks away from the radium atom, the latter looses 2 positive electric charges. As a consequence it must also loose 2 electrons from its outer electronic cloud. Radium has the atomic number 88, so the newly formed atom will be numbered 86, with 86 outer electrons to it. This atom, as a glance at table 2, (Appendix) will show, must be an atom with a completed electronic shell. Such an element (as we have seen before) is a gas because of the small forces which the completed electron shells exert on each other.

Here before our eyes a transmutation of the chemical elements is going on, naturally and spontaneously beyond the control of man. Radioactivity is a story of transmutation, one element changing into another and in doing so flinging out from its interior particles which move with immense speed. All radioactive matter eventually in the course of

Fig. 10. *THE DISINTEGRATION OF A RADIUM ATOM*

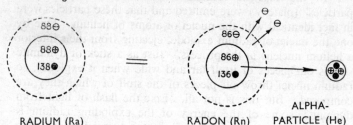

RADIUM (Ra)	RADON (Rn)	ALPHA-PARTICLE (He)
(number 88; weight 226)	(number 86; weight 222)	(number 2; weight 4)

A Radium atom disintegrates into one of Radon and an alpha-particle (Helium nucleus). Such changes of the atomic nuclei can be expressed in a convenient manner by a simple equation. For the reaction described in the diagram above we can write ;

$$226 \; Ra \atop 88 \qquad = \qquad 222 \; Rn \atop 86 \qquad + \qquad 4 \; He \atop 2$$

The symbols are those generally used for the chemical elements (see appendix I). The upper figures give the atomic weight and the lower ones the atomic number, that is the number of protons in the nucleus. The difference between these figures gives the number of neutrons in the nucleus.

millions of years will by this method be changed to lead, which is their final inactive product.

When the nucleus of radon breaks up it also emits an alpha-particle, which flies out at a speed of over 36 million miles an hour. The energy contained in this flying particle is immense. Every radon atom which spontaneously breaks up pumps out in this way more power than ever could be achieved in the most violent chemical explosive. Per atom disrupted, radioactive elements disgorge millions of times more energy than T.N.T. and it is only because they can be obtained in such small quantities and then break up quite slowly, that their tremendous energy has passed unnoticed until fifty years ago. When however the strength of their disruption is viewed from an atomic point of view, its greatness is ample evidence of atomic power. As an example, suppose a pound of radon gas could be obtained, then the total energy it would liberate in the form of fast moving alpha-particles would be about 800,000 kilowatt-hours, sufficient to raise 20 million cars as high as the roof of a house. All this energy, and much more again, lies hidden in the earth's crust in sufficient quantity to maintain by its production of energy nearly all the earth's inner heat, which we see at close range sometimes in volcanic power. It is not surprising, however, that all this energy lies dormant, unused by man; for, as the Curies found, it is a Herculean task to obtain even a grain or two of concentrated radioactive material. The nuclear power that we can employ to-day depends on uranium, a substance easier to extract than radium.

Since each time a radium atom blows up it is changed into radon, the total amount of radium in a lump of the metal vanishes gradually. After 1600 years the lump will only contain half the original amount of radium and after another 1600 years this will be again decreased by half, to a quarter of the original amount, and so on. This decay of the original substance is, of course, a general feature of all the radioactiv elements, and it is customary to speak of the " half value period " of a substance by which is meant the time after which half of the original number of atoms have disintegrated. For radium, as we have just seen, this time is 1600 years. Uranium which like radium emits alpha-particles decays even more slowly. In an ounce of uranium about 800,000 nuclei disintegrate per second, yet so vast is the total number of uranium atoms in an ounce that only half of them are changed after 4,500 million years. It is because its life time is so long, longer even than the existence of the earth as a separate globe, that it is still to be found at all. Such other radioactive elements as there may have been have decayed away early in the history of the earth.

There are of course many radioactive elements which have a very short life indeed, one for example decaying to half its powers in a millionth of a second. These brief unstable elements, however, like parasites, cannot live alone. They can only be found where their long-lived parent element lives as well. It is therefore the substances which have colossal life times, like uranium, that keep the whole radioactive system alive to-day. Their decay gives birth to three whole series of radioactive children, three families with the aged elements uranium, protactinium and thorium as progenitors (appendix, 3). These three are the heaviest elements remaining in the earth and one must presume that in time they and their radioactive descendants also will disappear.

When uranium disintegrates a new element is formed. This in turn breaks up and another radioactive product is created. So the process goes on, through no less than 13 different kinds of active elements, including radium amongst them, until in the end stability is reached and no further transformations can occur (appendix, 3). The final element is lead. The uranium nucleus, of weight 238, in throwing out an alpha-particle of weight 4, changes into an atom of weight 234. As each change occurs, each atom, in general, becomes lighter until in the end the weight of the lead produced is only 206. On the other hand, the lead produced by the disintegration of thorium and protactinium is of different weight. Actinium lead weighs per atom 207 and thorium lead 208. Of course, all lead whatever its parentage behaves in exactly the same way; chemically one kind of lead is indistinguishable from another. All lead atoms have the same number of electrons, their sole difference lies in the mass of their nuclei. Such materials as this, similar in chemical appearance but different in atomic weight, are called "isotopes," and their importance will be only too evident in the question of atomic energy. Here from the study of radioactivity, as Rutherford and Soddy were the first to show, an important new fact is brought to light concerning the make up of atoms. Different isotopes of each element can exist which appear chemically alike. Nearly all other elements besides lead have now been found to contain atoms of different weight, perhaps the most familiar to-day being "heavy water." Heavy water consists, just as ordinary water of molecules containing two hydrogen and one oxygen atom each, but the great difference is that each hydrogen atom has a weight 2 instead of the usual weight 1. By means of the convenient nomenclature (for nuclear processes) which we have already introduced (see fig. 10), the three lead isotopes can easily be distinguished as $^{206}_{82}$ Pb, $^{207}_{82}$ Pb and $^{208}_{82}$ Pb, while for the two different hydrogens we can write $^{1}_{1}$ H and $^{2}_{1}$ H.

The whole history of radioactivity is, as we have seen, one of energy changes, a spontaneous and natural production

URANIUMLEAD
(weight 206)   **ACTINIUMLEAD**
                          (weight 207)   **THORIUMLEAD**
                                                    (weight 208)

Fig. II. *Isotopes. Radioactive decay of the elements Uranium, Protoactinium and Thorium produces three different types atoms. They all have 82 protons but different numbers of neutrons. Since the number of protons (and with it the number of electrons in the cloud) determines the chemical properties, the three atoms are chemically alike. They are all lead atoms but differ in atomic weight.* (See Appendix, 3).

of power on a nuclear scale. It is a story of the ejection of fast particles and rays of various kinds out of unstable atoms. The process is always one of matter breaking down and never of building up. To the inquiring mind it is fascinating to imagine the possible results of actions carried out the other way. Instead of observing the changes that happen when nuclei break up, what might occur if instead energetic particles were artificially pumped in? Would it be possible *artificially* to change one element into a heavier one by attacking it with a high concentration of nuclear power? It was with such thoughts as these that Rutherford in 1919 started his celebrated and successful experiments on the first artificial transmutation of the elements. He knew, of course, that to overcome the intense electric forces which surround a nucleus, immensely energetic particles would have to be used. As his bombarding missiles therefore he chose the fast moving alpha-particles thrown out by radium. Moreover, as the electric fields around nuclei are less intense for atoms of low atomic number, he contented himself at first with nitrogen atoms as targets.

The results fulfilled all his expectations. Under such a heavy fire of alpha-particles, a few of the nitrogen nuclei were changed into the heavier nuclei of oxygen (plate VII).

Encouraged and fortified with the success of Rutherford's first experiment, it was not long before other workers

Fig. 12. THE FIRST ARTIFICIAL TRANSMUTATION

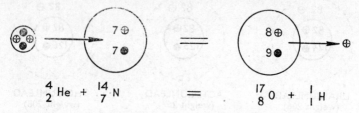

$$\frac{4}{2}He + \frac{14}{7}N \quad = \quad \frac{17}{8}O + \frac{1}{1}H$$

By bombarding the nuclei of nitrogen atoms with alpha-particles, Rutherford changed nitrogen into oxygen. At the bombardment the alpha-particle is taken up by the nucleus and a single proton is thrown out instead. Thus the newly formed nucleus contains 8 protons and is therefore oxygen (atomic number 8). The weight of this artificially created oxygen atom is, however, 17 and not 16 as that of ordinary oxygen. The new atom is an isotope of oxygen, containing one neutron more than the more common isotope with weight 16. For the sake of simplicity the electron-clouds are not shown in the diagram.

in almost every country in the world busied themselves with this new alchemy. Artificial transmutation of the elements was carried out here, there and everywhere. Not content with the natural sources of speedy alpha-particles supplied by radium, huge electrical machines were erected to provide "home-made" bombarding particles, and a whole new world of nuclear research began (appendix, 4). The first successful installation for the production of swiftly moving particles with which to attack atomic nuclei was set up in the Cavendish Laboratory in Cambridge, where Cockroft and Walton carried out in 1932 the first artificial transmutations of the elements lithium and boron. Some of us may remember the great stir this "splitting of the atom" caused in the daily press, due no doubt in part to the fact that for the first time it had been done without employing radium as the attacking weapon (plate VIII).

Cockcroft and Walton's artificial disintegration of lithium deserves particular attention. The lithium nuclei were bombarded with protons which had been given a high speed in the high voltage machine. The lithium nuclei broke up to form 2 helium nuclei each.

$$\frac{7}{3}Li + \frac{1}{1}H = \frac{4}{2}He + \frac{4}{2}He$$

The two helium nuclei, artificially created alpha-particles,

Fig. 13. ARTIFICIAL RELEASE OF ATOMIC ENERGY

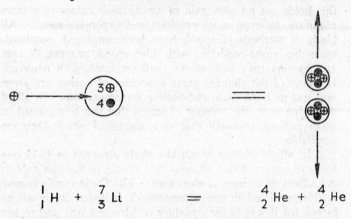

$$_1^1 H + {}_3^7 Li = {}_2^4 He + {}_2^4 He$$

When a proton is shot into a Lithium nucleus, 2 alpha-particles are formed which fly apart with an energy 40 times greater than the energy of the bombarding proton. Unfortunately so many protons have to be wasted before a single hit is scored that the whole process consumes much more energy than is produced.

were observed to fly apart in opposite directions with extreme violence (plate VII), and the energy of their motion was determined by careful experiments. It turned out to be more than 40 times that of the bombarding proton. The energy needed to break up the lithium nucleus was thus only 2.5% of the energy released in the subsequent disintegration.

At first it may appear as if these experiments had thrown open a new source of energy of fantastic dimensions. However, such artificial disintegration of atoms is a very rare event. Unfortunately protons cannot be aimed at the lithium nuclei but must be fired at random, and as a result only one proton in a million scored a bull's eye hit. So Cockcroft and Walton were forced to put from 10,000 to 100,000 times more energy into their machine than could have been derived from the disintegration of atoms in it.

By now the total number of different transmutations of one element into another which have been carried out artificially is so great that it would be difficult to count them all. Even artificial gold has been produced in this way, but this holds out no easy gain of wealth as it comes only from platinum, an even more precious and expensive metal. All kinds of methods of attack have been employed, bombardment by alpha-particles, with high-speed protons, X-rays and gamma rays and, as we shall see later, with neutrons. In many of the changes great quantities of energy are given out, just as happens in radioactive transmutations. In all of them, however, the number of atoms that can be changed is, as in radium, so small that as a source of power they are negligible.

In all this welter of activity there emerged in 1933 one more discovery which showed that poetic justice can rule in the affairs of science as elsewhere. The Curie family is now justly associated in consequence with radioactivity in *all* its facets, for it was to the daughter of Mmme Curie and to her son-in-law, Joliot, that the honour came of announcing to the world the first production of *artificial* radioactivity. They showed that, not only could nuclei be transmuted by artificial means, but also that by transmutation some nuclei became radioactive sources of their own. The first substance made was radioactive nitrogen which decayed itself away to half its radioactive power in only 11 minutes.

To-day very many new artificial radioactive elements are known. All have comparatively short lives; they can be easily produced and are in consequence of utmost value. A batch of radioactive salt can easily be made to have an activity as great as four or five grammes of radium and has already been put to good use in medical research. Radio-active isotopes can be traced because of the radiation which they emit. The body on the other hand selects atoms according to their chemical properties only, and does not distinguish between different isotopes of the same element. By putting into the food some radioactive atoms which can be traced because they are so to say " labelled." one can find out whether, where and how soon this food is taken up by the body. It is very probable that all these new radio-active elements existed on the earth long ago, but having such short lives they died soon after the earth cooled down. In the laboratory to-day they are recreated, perhaps for the first time for more than a thousand million years.

CHAPTER FOUR

WAVES, PARTICLES AND QUANTA

BY 1920 experiments on the structure of the atom had not only yielded the rough picture of a nucleus surrounded by electrons but had also provided a great accumulation of detailed knowledge. In particular the pattern of the electron cloud had been thoroughly investigated by spectroscopic methods and such gaps in the information as then existed were rapidly being filled by a veritable avalanche of research. Within a few years man's conception of the constitution of matter had completely changed. The solid bulk of a lump of iron as it appears to our senses had been replaced by the idea of a flimsy framework of madly gyrating particles, separated from each other by a vast expanse of space. Light and colour, electricity and magnetism had acquired a new meaning through the opening of the sub-atomic world.

However, in spite of all these advances the atomic picture remained strangely empty. It had soon been discovered that in order to give a satisfactory interpretation of atomic phenomena certain rules had to be obeyed. These rules, which in most cases had been established by trial and error, had no counterpart in other fields of physics. Moreover certain observations could not be reconciled at all with the new atomic model, and as time went on the number of these observations increased steadily. There was no doubt that in the main the picture sketched by Rutherford and Bohr was correct, but its true meaning remained obscure.

Such situations have occurred again and again in the history of science. Whenever a great stride forward is achieved, it is discovered only too soon that the knowledge gained is but half the truth and that a new idea has to be provided to instill life into the model which has been developed. When Copernicus took the earth out of the centre of the universe and relegated it to a modest orbit

49

around the sun, he created a new world in which the complicated movements of the planets could be reduced to simple concentric circles. From the scientific point of view the new model of the solar system was an enormous success. Galileo showed that the planet Jupiter is surrounded by satellites which move around the main body as the planets circle around the sun. Kepler found a simple relation between the time taken by the planets to complete one orbit and their distance from the sun.

Copernicus, Galileo and Kepler had created out of their observations a model of the solar system which stated accurately *how* the planets and satellites move in orbits around central bodies but they were unable to say *why*. The answer to this why was given by Newton when he connected the movements of the astronomical bodies with the action of an unseen force, gravitation. He showed that the sun's attraction provides the reason for the planetary orbits and he thus gave meaning and content to the Copernican model, the correctness of which had been proved before Newton's time but which was not understood.

A situation, similar to that in astronomy before Newton, arose in the field of natural history at the beginning of the last century when the work of Linnaeus and Cuvier revealed amazing similarities between the different species of plants and animals. They developed a classified system comprising not only all the varied forms of life which exist at present but also the remains of plants and animals long extinct. Meaning to this system, however, was only given by the work of Darwin, when he showed that the reason for the similarities is to be found in the fact that all the species had been developed by a process of evolution from common ancestors.

Even before the full extent of the import of radioactivity had been grasped, doubts in the validity of the known principles of physics began to be expressed. The German physicist Planck, when trying to describe the phenomena of radiation by a general law, had come across a most disturbing fact. In the year 1900 he announced that he had found a formula, but that it implied that energy was not radiated in the form of a continuous stream but in small indivisible energy parcels which he called " quanta." In other words, he postulated that the rays of the sun, or for that matter those emitted by any source of radiation, are composed of tiny atoms of energy, and that the only reason why light and heat appear to us as a continuous flow is the extreme smallness of the energy quanta. Just as our senses are not capable of perceiving single atoms but only agglomerations of huge numbers of them, so they fail us when we try to distinguish individual quanta of radiation. According to Planck, the energy quanta are not all of equal size but vary with the wavelength of the radiation. The shorter the wavelength, the greater are the quanta. Those of red light are smaller than the quanta of blue and violet light and these in turn are smaller than those of ultra-violet light and X-rays. This means that the energy parcels thrown out by an X-ray are bigger than those coming from the sun and that the sun's rays contain bigger energy parcels than the red glow of an electric fire. Planck's theory also offers an explanation for the curious fact, mentioned in Chapter 2, that the hotter an explosion is, the more blueish is the glare emanating from it. For the heat produced in any reaction is a measure of the liberated energy, and big energy changes produce big quanta.

Planck's formula, introducing the conception of quanta, involved a flat contradiction of well-established principles of physics and the first reaction of the scientific world was to treat it as a mathematical oddity without much physical meaning. However, experiments designed to establish the existence of these quanta were undertaken and proved eminently successful. Soon there was no doubt that Planck's ideas were correct and in the past 30 years his ideas have proved their value not only in physics but also in chemistry and biology. It is known, for instance, that children develop rickets because they suffer from lack of vitamin D. This substance can be produced in the human body itself through the effect of sunlight, but the chemical reaction involved requires a fairly big energy quantum, such as is contained in ultra-violet light. Sunrays, any amount of them, when passed through a glass window, which is known to cut out ultra-violet rays, will fail to stop rickets. On the other hand, a small dose of radiation administered with an ultra-violet lamp will be sufficient to prevent or cure the disease. Thus an abstruse conception in the field of theoretical physics had found its application in the domain of infant welfare.

Bohr's atomic model was designed to forge a link between the quantum theory of radiation and man's conception of the properties of matter. It had long been known that atoms in hot gases emit light of only certain wavelengths, that is only quanta of definite size. This can be shown by a very simple experiment. A few grains of table salt put into a gas flame will give it a bright yellow colour, because the sodium atoms produce energy quanta of one particular size only, corresponding to the wavelength of yellow light. Bohr's explanation of this phenomenon is to be found in the size of the orbits in which an electron can move around the nucleus. According to his assumptions, electrons can change their orbits. For instance, if one atom collides vehemently with another one, as happens in a hot gas, one of the outermost electrons may be pushed away from its parent atom into an orbit with a greater diameter than the one previously occupied. Soon, however, it will slip back into its old path and in doing so, it will emit a quantum of light. The fact that always the same wavelength of light, that is the same energy quantum, is emitted in the process shows that the electron cannot be pushed out to any orbit of arbitrary size but jumps only from one definite orbit into another.

Let us take the simplest case, that of a hydrogen atom possessing only one electron (fig. 14). From the orbit nearest to the nucleus the electron can be pushed into orbits 2, 3, 4, and so on and it can jump back from a distant orbit into one of the nearer ones. However, it cannot circle in any other than these " quantum " orbits, as for instance in an intermediate one, 2a, between 2 and 3. The size of the quantum orbits is determined by the same mathematical quantity, called Planck's constant, which appears in Planck's radiation formula.

Here we encounter the first important difference between the Bohr model and the solar system. Let us return for a moment to the picture of the earth moving round in the energy trough of the sun (p. 33). If the speed, and with it the energy, of the earth were to rise or to fall a little, the

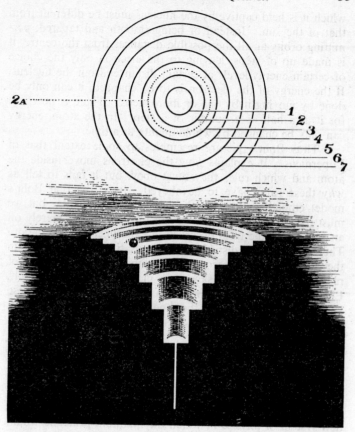

Fig. 14. *THE ELECTRON IN THE ENERGY TROUGH WHICH IS CREATED BY THE ELECTRICAL ATTRACTION OF THE PROTON IN THE HYDROGEN ATOM*

earth would take up an orbit slightly bigger or smaller than its present one. The walls of the gravitational trough are smooth and consequently, corresponding to the energy which it may possess, the earth could take up *any* position along the walls of the trough. It could rotate in an orbit of *any* size around the sun. The electron, as we have just seen, is limited to certain definite orbits and the energy trough in which it is held captive by the nucleus must be different from that of the sun. Instead of being smooth and tapered, permitting orbits at all the possible distances from the centre, it is made up of steps, leaving to the electron only the choice of certain energy levels at certain distances from the nucleus. If the energy of the electron is to be changed, it can only be done by moving it by one or more steps. There is no room for it at a half or a quarter of a step. In the atom, energy can only be changed by whole quanta at a time.

Thus Bohr's picture resembles to some extent that of Copernicus. It explains *how* the electrons move inside the atom and which rules they must obey, but it fails to tell us *why* these rules have to be obeyed. It is true that Bohr's model embodies Planck's theory of energy quanta, but we must remember that this theory in turn was based merely on an analysis of the facts observed in experiments on radiation. There were other disturbing and unsatisfactory features in the Bohr model, irreconcilable with the known laws of physics, which nobody saw more clearly than Bohr himself. Electrons circling round in orbits should according to these laws produce radiation all the time, which in fact they do not, the generation of light being attributed by Bohr only to jumps from one orbit to the other.

The quantum theory constituted a break with the accepted system of physics now called " classical " physics, but it soon turned out to be only the first step into a new world with new and unfamiliar laws; the world of quanta. Physicists began to realise that somewhere before them lay a new system of physics in which the quantum principle would have its due place and out of which the strange rules established by Bohr would emerge as necessary consequences. To find the key to this new system meant finding the place where classical physics was at fault. Somewhere in the logical development of physical laws and principles a mistake had occurred which had led finally to the discrepancies between these laws and the observed facts.

The observations themselves provided the clue to where the fault was to be found. It was quite clear that classical physics in general proved adequate except when its rules were applied to the world of very small dimensions. Only when trying to explain the behaviour of atoms and molecules were scientists faced with the breakdown of their accepted methods.

At about the same time as the quantum problem began to menace the system of classical physics, another threat to its foundation had arisen. Einstein in his theory of relativity had shown that the laws of Newtonian mechanics, which explained so satisfactorily the happenings in our accustomed world, became invalid once extremely high speeds and vast dimensions were concerned. He pointed out that the laws of mechanics were based on observations in a world of human dimensions and of motions slow enough to be perceived with our senses. For such a world these laws will be valid, but one must not expect them to hold under conditions far removed from normal human experience. The new laws of motion of the relativistic world framed by Einstein become identical with Newton's laws when they are applied to the range of speed for which Newton's laws were formulated.

In the atomistic world, too, physicists had treated atoms and electrons like bits of matter as they are encountered in everyday life, like billiard balls or marbles. They endowed their electronic and protonic billiard balls with minute size and electric charges, but nevertheless the objects concerned remained—billiard balls. Similarly they thought of light waves as ripples on the surface of a pond. Since Maxwell's time it has been realised that light is an electromagnetic vibration but man can neither see, feel, hear, taste or smell an electromagnetic field and so in the back of his mind there remained the picture of ripples on a pond. Just as in relativity these everyday ideas must be abandoned, so man must resign himself to the fact that he cannot conceive in his imagination the nature of things outside those dimensions which he reaches with his senses. Now and then it may be possible to devise a model for processes on the atomic scale such as the miniature solar system of Bohr and Rutherford, but nevertheless electrons are neither billiard balls nor planets, and it is thus not surprising that they fail to obey the rules obeyed by these immeasurably bigger objects.

Scientists, however did not easily abandon the pretty

world of atomic imagination. In penetrating into quantum territory, an exploration which is by no means finished yet, valiant attempts have been made from time to time by intrepid physicists to bring back to the land of normal human understanding trophies of their quest in the shape of the laid ghost of a quantum or the true likeness of an electron. Only gradually did they learn that the new physical system has to be bought at the cost of all models and analogies. Quantumland has turned out to be an enchanted kingdom of mathematical descriptions, which vanish into nothing when their spell is broken by comparing them with billiard balls, ripples and roundabouts.

One of the knottiest problems of atomic physics is that of the energy quanta. In classical physics waves of light are regarded as electromagnetic ripples passing out into space and becoming weaker and weaker as they encompass an ever increasing volume. If we try to reconcile this picture with Planck's conception of indivisible energy quanta, we arrive at a strange conclusion. Taking a screen of given size, say one inch square, further and further away from a source of illumination, the amount of light received on the screen will continually get less. In the end, when very far away, the whole screen will only receive one quantum at a time and one should assume that the quantum will be spread out evenly over the whole screen. On the other hand, it is known that light waves can liberate electrons from a metal surface, a fact of which use is made in photo-cells. Clearly in order to do this, the quantum must be concentrated on a single electron and one can hardly expect that electrons will be liberated if each individual quantum is spread over a considerable part of the metal surface. In other words, a photo-cell should not work in very weak light. Nevertheless it does. The inescapable conclusion is that quanta do not spread out as they move away into space but that light really consists of a shower of energy parcels which behave very much like ordinary particles in that they retain their size and do not thin out indefinitely in space. Indeed it has been found possible and for many purposes convenient to describe the phenomena of radiation as being due to such particles of energy or "photons" as they are called.

Fig. 15. *PASSING MATTER AND WAVES THROUGH A SIEVE*

What then is light? Particles or waves? The same question has been asked in Newton's time until at last irrefutable evidence gained the day for the wave theory. This evidence is still valid to-day but it is now confronted with the equally irrefutable evidence for the particle-like behaviour of photons.

The peculiar double life of the light quanta which appear to be particles to-day and waves to-morrow induced physicists to suspect a still stranger relation. Since light waves behave occasionally like particles, they argued, is it not possible that particles may go about in the guise of waves? In 1924 Prince Louis de Broglie published a theory according to which moving particles of matter should be accompanied by waves, but the physical significance of these "matter-waves" remained obscure. In spite of this obscurity, the theory led to one of the greatest triumphs of modern physics. Three years later an experiment was performed which demonstrated that a shower of particles of matter does behave exactly like a wave.

This new and startling physical fact was discovered at about the same time by Davisson and Germer in America and G.P. (now Sir George) Thomson in Britain. Their experiments fundamentally consisted in the passing of electrons through a very fine sieve, and the results obtained were so strange that we should first examine what would be expected from such a process. If a thin stream of sand falls on to a sieve, some of the grains will pass right through without touching the mesh. Others will strike the mesh and bounce off, and so be scattered. The amount of scattering will depend on the relative size of grain and mesh, the finer the mesh the more widely will the grains be scattered. However, whether the mesh is fine or coarse, the general pattern formed by the grains after passing the sieve will always be the same. The majority of grains will fall near the centre, underneath the place where the stream hits the sieve and the further one goes away from the centre the smaller the chance for a particle to fall. If a moist black cloth is spread under the sieve, the grains will stick to the spot where they fall and the result of the experiment therefore will be a light patch of sand which is brightest in the centre, thinning out gradually toward the sides. Such is the pattern which classical physics associates with the passage of matter through a sieve.

The corresponding experiment of passing light waves through a sieve is performed with even greater ease. It is merely necessary to observe a distant street lamp through the fabric of an umbrella. The result is very different from the previous one. Instead of a patch of light dying away evenly from the centre we see a regular pattern of light spots, divided from each other by darkness. The reason for this is that the rays of light are scattered by the threads of the fabric, spreading out from their original direction. However, being waves by nature their effect when they meet again is not a simple additive one as that of the grains of sand. Wherever the crest of a wave meets another crest the resulting wave will be particularly strong and a light spot will appear, but where a crest encounters a trough the two will cancel each other out. At such a place there will be no wave at all, and darkness will result. How such a " diffraction " pattern is produced can easily be demonstrated by creating two interfering sets of waves on a water surface (plate IV).

Thus waves passed through a sieve behave differently from particles. In fact, the experiment just mentioned was used by Young and Fresnel to demonstrate irrefutably the wave nature of light, disposing as it seemed then, once and for all, of Newton's particle concept. The natural experiment, therefore, to make in order to decide on the existence of de Broglie's matter waves was to send elementary particles—electrons—through a very fine sieve. Very fine sieves are fortunately provided by nature in the form of crystals in which the regular arrangement of atoms provides an extremely narrow mesh just wide enough for electrons to pass through. This convenient mesh had already been used many years before to produce diffraction patterns of X-rays, patterns which look exactly like a street lamp seen through an umbrella. The result of sending a beam of electrons through a crystal and on to a photographic plate was staggering beyond belief. The pattern produced was identical with that obtained with light waves and X-rays (plate IV).

De Broglie's theory, which had received a very sceptical response when it was first proposed, turned out to be a resounding success. Electron waves emerged straight from the narrow confines of theoretical speculation into the field of practical application. They can be bent by a magnetic or an electric field just as light waves can be deviated in glass, and an instrument operated with electron rays containing magnetic lenses has been perfected. This is the electron microscope which has already proved a most valuable tool, opening up new views into the sub-microscopic world.

As regards the model of the atom, de Broglie's theory and its confirmation opened entirely new but very disturbing prospects. The double life of energy quanta, half waves, half particles, had not helped to make the riddle of atomic structure any less puzzling. To find the same dual nature in the elementary bits of matter was even more disconcerting. It sealed finally the fate of the model which pictured the atom as a miniature solar system populated by tiny billiard balls. Brilliant hypothesis and ingenious experiments had opened a view into the quantum world, but, to say the least, the outlook was unsettled. The whole position of physics was at that time aptly characterised by the late Sir William Bragg when he said: " We teach the wave theory on Mondays, Wednesdays and Fridays, and the particle conception on Tuesdays, Thursdays and Saturdays."

To overcome this dilemma an entirely new method for the description of physical phenomena was developed. Its function and the outstanding result obtained with it will play an important part in our narrative. However, before we enter further into the strange realm of quantum physics, we must mention its most startling outcome, Dirac's theory, which makes the relations between radiation and matter appear in a quite new light.

In his interpretation of the universe, man has progressively reduced the multifarious aspects of his world to simpler and more general ones. The infinite and bewildering variety of matter whether inorganic or animated was demonstrated to be nothing but the various ways of arranging a mere 92 different atoms, and these in turn were split up into only three elementary particles. At the same time the great variety of radiations, light, heat, ultra-violet, X-rays and gamma-rays was recognized to be merely different manifestations of electro-magnetic waves, all similar in character and only differing from each other in wavelength. Finally the photo-effect, electron diffraction and a number of other discoveries began to obliterate the difference between the two fundamental physical phenomena, matter and radiation.

The last link connecting the two was forged by Dirac, when in 1930 he came forward with an interpretation of the constitution of space and matter which by its boldness and its far-reaching consequences provoked incredulity and scepticism. By embodying the principles of relativity in his theory of particles and quanta, he arrived at a set of mathematical equations which fully and accurately describe the manner in which electrons behave. But apart from these solutions which correspond to the behaviour of particles as we know it, there appear in his theory others which did not seem to have a counterpart in the world of physical realities. The mathematical world which Dirac created on paper is one of beautiful symmetry. In it there exists the conception of negative mass as well as that of positive mass, the mass of material things which we can see and feel. It is not easy to grasp what is the meaning of a negative billiard ball, a negative cup of tea or an electron of negative mass. However, in our present times of scarcity we are perhaps more acutely aware of the significance of the minus sign than other generations were. Negative houses and negative foods have made their appearance all over the world, and we know them only too well. They are houses and foods which are *not there*. Just as the larders of the world are crowded with negative foods, so Dirac's universe is filled with negative matter, that is, empty space. According to his theory the vacuum which separates the stars and nebulae of the universe is packed with electrons of negative mass from which material electrons, the electrons we observe with our senses or instruments, stand out as a small residue. This residue, too, it appears, is destined to vanish in time into the all engulfing ocean of negative matter.

This whole picture will surely appear to the reader as a fantastic dream, a physicists nightmare, completely removed from reality. Even physicists, while appreciating the elegance of Dirac's interpretation, refused to accept his theory. Many of them realised with a sigh of relief that the theory dealt with things which on principle could not be observed, and they decided that an interpretation of the universe, the correctness of which could be neither proved or disproved, need not disturb the peace of their minds. That illusion, however, was shattered within two years.

While it is true that on the whole Dirac's universe is filled with negative mass, the existence of which can never be perceived, there must be some exceptions. There is still with us the residue of positive mass which constitutes our material world, and which so far has not found its place among the negative masses. The state of affairs has been compared with the picture presented by the stalls of an opera house before the curtain rises. Most of the seats have already been occupied and their occupants can be likened to the electrons of negative mass which almost fill the universe. They have vanished from the world of observable quantities. However, there are still a number of conspicuous late comers who are looking for their seats. These are the electrons which, because of their positive mass, are still open to observation. They are the building bricks of matter which make up the stars, the sun and the pages of this book. Besides the seated and the wandering electrons there are the empty seats, waiting for the latter. In the universe these empty seats, not yet occupied by electrons, must appear as " holes " in the vacuum. A hole in the vacuum is clearly a place which must be distinguishable from the void, and so, said Dirac, it must be something that can be observed.

These holes in empty space, fit to receive electrons, will themselves appear like electrons, but as electrons with a *positive electric charge*. When an ordinary electron meets such a " hole " in the universe, the two will combine and their place will be taken by empty space; mass will vanish. In our analogy it means that a late comer has found his seat and disappeared from the number of conspicuous wanderers.

Like all comparisons, this one is not complete. When an ordinary electron and a hole combine and their masses disappear, some trace is left. From the meeting of the two a parcel of radiant energy moves out into space, bearing witness to the disappearance of matter. Mass vanishes and energy is born. The obvious question that must follow is whether the reverse process, the disappearance of energy and the birth of mass, can also occur. Can a quantum of light vanish and leave as its only trace two electrons, one ordinary one and the other with a positive charge? If so, one should be able to observe these positive electrons.

The unequivocal answer to this question was given in 1932 when Anderson in America and shortly afterwards Blackett in England experimentally discovered positive electrons. They are found to be produced when cosmic rays, quanta of radiation which reach us from the unknown depths of the universe, are stopped by collision with matter. A light quantum sometimes disappears, and in its stead a pair of electrons is created, one with negative and the other with positive electric charge (plate VI). The positive electron, or positron as it is called, soon meets another ordinary electron and the two combine to form a pair of light quanta. This process, too, has been observed.

Fig. 16. *BIRTH AND DEATH OF MATTER*

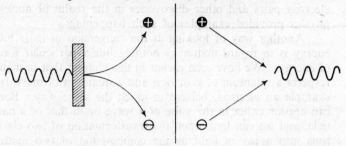

When an electro-magnetic wave (gamma-ray) is stopped, energy disappears and a positive and a negative electron are born. When a positive and a negative electron collide, they disappear and energy in the form of a gamma-ray is born.

Thus Dirac's fantastic theory was removed from the realm of speculation to that of reality, even if it was not proved in all its aspects. With their own eyes physicists could watch the birth and death of matter. It appears that our part of the universe has an abundance of negatively charged electrons, but it is possible that in other regions, so far unknown to us, matter may consist of atoms with negatively charged nuclei surrounded by positive electrons. Negatively charged protons however, have not been observed up to now, and their existence does not follow necessarily from Dirac's theory. The modern conception of the nucleus on the other hand does not exclude the possibility that the proton itself may change, but this is a question which we will leave open for the present.

The most surprising aspect of Dirac's theory but one that was least shocking to physicists, is the destruction and creation of matter. More than 40 years ago Einstein, in his formulation of the theory of relativity, derived an equation which postulated that mass and energy are equivalent. In this way the laws of conservation of mass and energy were combined. Instead of assuming that mass and energy are each indestructible, Einstein stated that they can be transformed one into another, and that only the sum total of mass and energy in the universe remains the same. What form this transformation might take and whether it really could occur remained a mystery for a long time, until the birth of electron pairs and other discoveries in the realm of nuclear physics provided examples of such happenings.

Another way of looking at the conversion of mass into energy is to regard matter as nothing but a particular form of energy. We have seen earlier in this chapter that in many respects a quantum of radiation and a quantum of mass, for example an electron, behave in much the same way. Both can appear either in the guise of a wave or in that of a particle, and we can look upon the transformation of two electrons into a ray of light as the combination of two matter waves into a light wave. It would, of course, be equally correct to refer to the transformation as a combination of two material particles into a pair of photons.

It seems that, mislead by his senses, man has failed up to the present to recognise the sublime simplicity of his physical world. With the identity of particles and waves, and the equivalence of mass and energy, physics has taken a further, and possibly the last, step in the unification of the phenomena which make up the universe. Its only content, energy, continually deludes our perception by appearing now as matter and then as radiation.

Plate I.—PIONEERS

Pierre Curie Marie Curie Lord Rutherford Niels Bohr

 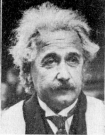  

r George Thomson Albert Einstein Sir James Chadwick F. W. Aston

Harold C. Urey Enrico Fermi Frederic Joliot Otto Hahn

Plate II.—1896

Top left. (*a*) *In 1896 Henri Becquerel discovered a strange radiation emanating from the mineral pitchblende (see p. 39).*

Below. (*b*) *A piece of pitchblende photographed in daylight (left) and (right) the imprint made on a photographic plate by the rays emanating from it.* (Sir William Crookes.)

(*c*) *The " laboratory " where radium was discovered (see p. 40).* (Eve Curie.)

Plate III.—1946

Top. (a) *Hanford Plutonium Plant, near Pasco, Washington* (see p. 163).

Left. (b) *Separation of Pitchblende concentrate at the Eldorado Mine, North-Western Canada* (see p. 143).

Above. (c) *Isotope separation plant at Clinton, Oak Ridge, Tennessee* (see p. 148).

Plate IV.—WAVES AND PARTICLES

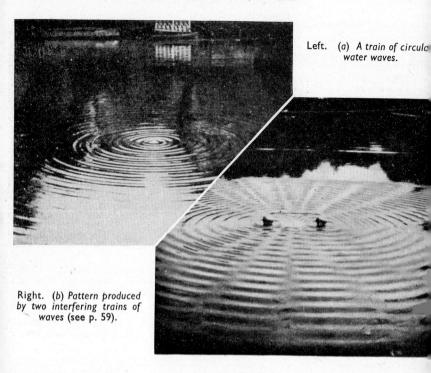

Left. (a) A train of circular water waves.

Right. (b) Pattern produced by two interfering trains of waves (see p. 59).

(c) and (d) Diffraction patterns produced by X-rays (left) and electrons (right) (see p. 59).

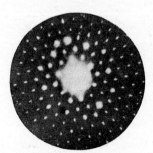

Plate V.—THE OLD PARTICLES

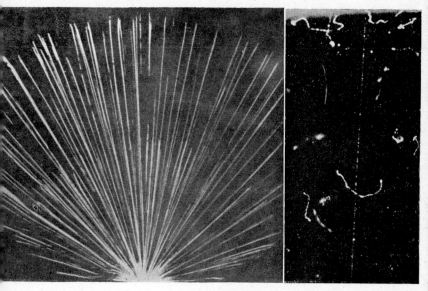

Above. (a) *Cloud chamber tracks of alpha particles of two different ranges coming from a mixture of thorium C and C¹ (see p. 93).*

Above. (b) *Beta-particles (electrons) (see p. 82). The straight track is produced by a fast particle while the tracks of slow electrons are irregular.*

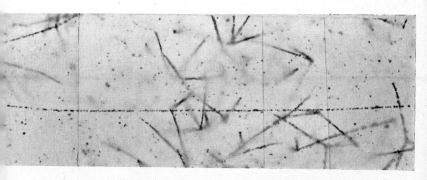

Above. (c) *Micro-photograph of a proton track in photographic emulsion. The kinks in the track indicate deflections of the proton by the positive charge of other nuclei (see p. 123).*

Plate VI.—THE NEW PARTICLES

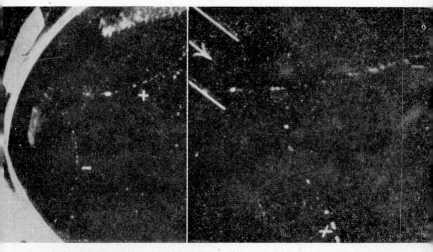

Above. (a) and (b) Birth of matter. Pairs of positive and negative electrons being created by gamma-rays in a metal plate (left) and in a gas (right). The arrow indicates the direction of the incident gamma-radiation. The paths of the electrons are bent in opposite directions by a magnetic field (see p. 62).

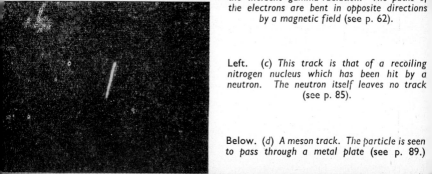

Left. (c) This track is that of a recoiling nitrogen nucleus which has been hit by a neutron. The neutron itself leaves no track (see p. 85).

Below. (d) A meson track. The particle is seen to pass through a metal plate (see p. 89.)

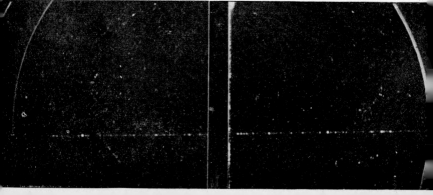

*Plate VII.—*NUCLEAR REACTIONS

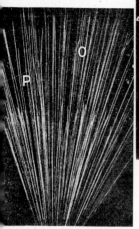

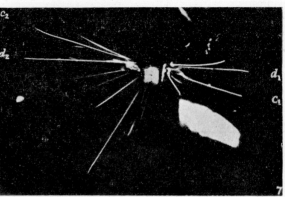

Above. (b) *Bombardment of lithium with protons. Pairs of helium nuclei are formed (c_1 c_2, d_1 d_2) which fly off in opposite directions (see p. 47).*

...ove. (a) *Disintegration of* ...ogen. *One of the bombard-* ...alpha-particles *changes a* ...ogen *nucleus into an oxygen* ...leus (O) *and a proton* (P) *(see p. 45).*

...ight. (c) *Fission of uranium under neutron* ...mbardment. *In a film of uranium oxide a* ...anium *nucleus has been broken up (at the point* ...dicated by the arrow) *into two fragments which* ...e *shot out in opposite directions. The branches* ...e *due to collision of the fragments with other* *atoms (see p. 133). (Physical Review.)*

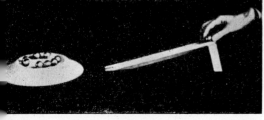

Left. (d) *Bohr's model of nuclear reactions.*

Plate VIII.—THE TOOLS (I)

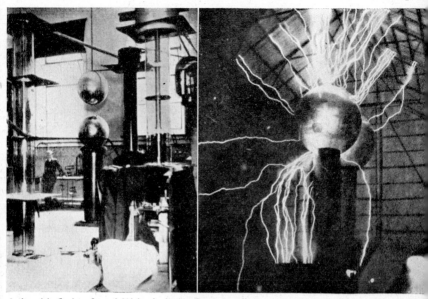

Left. (a) Cockcroft and Walton's high voltage installation with which the first artificial transmutations were carried out (see p. 46). Right. (b) Sparks from a 5,000,000-volt Van de Graaff high voltage generator. (M.I.T.)

Left. (c) The cyclotron, an apparatus invented by E. O. Lawrence, in which positively charged particles can be accelerated without the use of high voltages. Below, a close-up of the emerging beam of deuterons. Right. (d) The betatron, an installation for the acceleration of electrons (see p. 171).

Plate IX.—THE TOOLS (II)

Left. (a) Aston's original mass spectrograph. 'M' is the electro-magnet in the field of which the path of the ions bent (see p. 130).

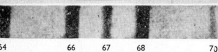

64   66   67   68   70

Above. (b) Five isotopes of zinc, with the weights 64, 66, 67, 68 and 70, separated in the mass spectrograph. The degree of blackening indicates the relative abundance of the isotopes (see p. 146).

Right. (c) The cloud chamber (see p. 84). The tracks are photographed by the camera above.

Plate X.—July 16th, 1945, 5.30 a.m.

(a) and (b) Two phases in the explosion of the trial bomb in the New Mexican Desert (see p. 150). Since the bomb was detonated close to the ground the soil was rendered radioactive for several weeks.

(c) Trial explosion of an atomic bomb under water at Bikini Lagoon on July 25th, 1946.

Plate XI.—A BOMB IS DROPPED

Blast and radiation have killed about 100,000 people. Dust and smoke rise high above the clouds into the sub-stratosphere. Radioactive atoms are scattered by the wind over an area as large as Australia.

Plate XII.—EXPLODING STARS

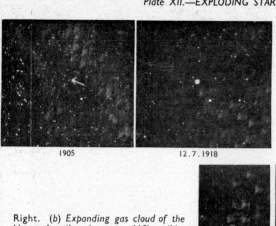

1905   12.7.1918

Left. (a) A Nova bursts into light. The Nova Aquilæ before and after the explosion in 1918 (see p. 113). (Yerkes Obs.)

Right. (b) Expanding gas cloud of the Nova Acquilæ (see p. 113). (Mt. Wilson Photo.)

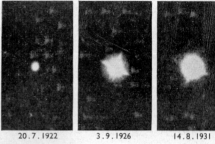

20.7.1922   3.9.1926   14.8.1931

8.5.1901   16.4.1915

Left. (c) A Super-Nova flares up in a distant galaxy. The spiral nebula N.G.C.4527 before and after the outburst (see p. 114). (Lick Obs.)

Right. (d) The brightest star ever observed. A Super-Nova in the galaxy I.C. 4182, which is 3 million light years away. It outshone the sun 300 million times. (Mt. Palomar Photo.)

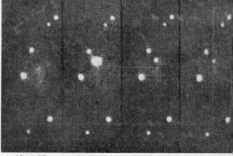

10.4.37   26.8.37   31.12.37   8.6.38

CHAPTER FIVE

PROBABILITY

WE started our narrative with a description of the atomic model, a nucleus surrounded by electrons, and in this generalised form we can let it stand. More detailed ideas about the structure and the nature of the elementary building bricks, models which are based on analogies with things perceived by our senses, can, however, have no place in the atomic world. Theory and experiment have shown that no further headway could be expected in the field of atomic physics unless a system was evolved in which the wave and particle aspects of radiation and matter are reconciled. It cannot be the fault of an electron if it appears in some experiments as a particle and in others as a wave. The mistake, as we have seen, must be in the method of description. It is wrong to say that electrons are waves because they behave like ripples on a pond when passing through a crystal, or that photons, are particles, billiard balls or bullets, because they behave like them when they fall on a photo-cell. Ripples on a pond and billiard balls are things of the macroscopic world to which we are accustomed and whose behaviour we can predict by the empirical laws we have found for them. To find and understand the laws which rule the behaviour of elementary particles, the principles of mechanics, which give laws suitable only for billiard balls and water waves, will be of little use. In order to continue the assault on the atom, a new scientific method, based on observations of events in the world of quanta, had to be found. This new method of description, called quantum—or wave-mechanics began with the work of de Broglie, and in the twenty years of its existence has yielded results which have far surpassed the keenest hopes.

The shattering blows which had been dealt to the once proud edifice of classical physics made physicists look round to see what could be salvaged from the wreck. Billiard balls and water waves even in disguised and refined forms were of course unacceptable and so were many of the laws of mechanics. For a time demolition squads roamed through the house of physics, tearing down much of the structure and regarding with covetous eyes such treasured possessions as the laws of conservation of energy and of mass. Meanwhile the new building was started with such material as seemed to be uncontaminated with the rot. Previous experience in a similar upheaval, created by the theory of relativity, had shown that the axioms and principles of mathematics were extremely shockproof and that, if applied with discretion, they would provide excellent material for the new structure. In fact, it was argued, if physicists were to stick solely to mathematical methods of description, mishaps like those with the particle and wave picture could not possibly happen.

Thus quantum physics arose as a method of description in which the movements of electrons or photons are not compared with those of billiard balls or water waves but are circumscribed only by a set of mathematical equations. It is true that now and then there appears an event in the quantum world which bears a faint resemblance to things which we can grasp with the imagination, but in general the events have no counterpart in the sphere of human experience. A complete understanding of quantum-mechanics demands the ability to follow the logic of mathematical operations and to appreciate the physical significance of algebraic formulae.

However, there is no reason for non-mathematicians to despair. Once it is clearly understood that the method of quantum mechanics does not permit easy and close analogies, we can proceed in our account of the atomic world, admittedly with some difficulty, but nevertheless with a certain measure of comprehension. Now and then we will still be able to make use of the primitive conceptions of particles and waves in order to describe the behaviour of protons, electrons and photons, provided we do not use these subterfuges for conclusive reasoning. Neither will the mathematical nature of the new physics debar us completely from understanding the striking and satisfactory results which have been achieved through its application. The strange aspect of many of these results is not so much due to the mathematical form in which they are clothed as to their novelty. New and unaccustomed facts always make a greater demand on our powers of comprehension than the events of everyday life. A mere 150 years ago the phenomena of electricity were vague and incomprehensible and their very existence was doubted by a great many people. Some scientific treatises of the eighteenth century describe lighting as caused by the collision of " nitrous " and " sulphurous " clouds. The authors were clearly unwilling to invoke a strange and doubtful new force like electricity merely to account for a rare phenomenon as a thunderstorm. To-day electricity has completely ceased to be mysterious. Familiarity has bred contempt and any bright boy of ten is quite competent in dealing with broken switches and blown fuses. He knows very well how electricity behaves. It is likely that the bright boys of a hundred years hence will deal with quanta and electron waves in much the same way. Let us hope that they will laugh at their great-grandparents who had to consult a book in order to grasp the secrets of the atom.

Even before it was confirmed by experiment, de Broglie's theory of matter-waves gave a strong impetus to the further development of quantum physics. By treating them as waves Schrödinger took up the interpretation of electrons and protons where the particle description had failed. He worked out what would happen when the wave which represents an electron encounters a proton. This wave, or more accurately this little packet of waves, is diffracted by the proton just as light waves are diffracted when passing through the fabric of an umbrella. In some cases the electron wave will be bent right round the proton, forming a ring shaped pattern such as is obtained when a beam of light falls on a small object. We often see such rings before our eyes when we look into the sky. They are caused by the diffraction of light on tiny specks of dust which have settled on the pupil of the eye. The electron wave, representing a negative charge, will then remain with the positive proton, surrounding it like a little ring. A hydrogen atom has been formed.

Waves, however, have their peculiarities. For example, the waves which can be created in one's bath tub by bobbing up and down in it are strictly determined by the size of the

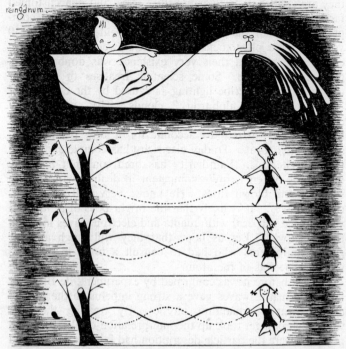

Fig. 17. *THESE WAVELENGTHS ARE MOST FAVOURED*

bath and the amount of water. More convincing and less messy experiments on wave formation can be conducted by wriggling a short length of rope the other end of which is securely fastened. The simplest pattern is the one used in skipping in which the length of the rope is made to swing in half a wave-length. With some practice one can produce vibrations with a full wavelength, three halves and even two full wavelengths. It is clear, however, that only certain definite vibrations can be set up which depend on the length of the rope. This property of a string to permit only certain characteristic waves to be set up in it provides also the physical basis of such musical instruments as the violin or the piano.

The electron wave, also, is limited to such definite vibrations whose character is determined by the nature of electron and proton. Electron waves around a proton can form only certain rings and Schrödinger was able to show that these diffraction rings are exactly the orbits which the Bohr model attributed to the electron in the hydrogen atom.

This is much more than just another way of interpreting atomic structure. We remember that the Bohr model showed that electrons move around the nucleus in certain particular orbits but it failed in explaining why these orbits are selected. By representing the electronic orbits as the *natural diffraction pattern* of the electron wave, Schrödinger's wave mechanics not only provided a conclusive reason for the existence of these definite orbits, it also gave new meaning to the structure of the atom.

So far we have referred to diffraction *rings* around the nucleus in order to keep the picture as simple as possible. In reality the model has not two but three dimensions and consequently the electron wave envelops the nucleus like a shell. Nevertheless, it is more convenient to retain the simpler conception of rings which will not lead us into any difficulties provided we remember that a section of the electron shell appears as a ring just as the peel of an orange which has been cut in half appears circular in form.

The diffraction rings of the electron wave differ in a number of ways from the old conception of planetary orbits. They present a diffuse pattern instead of well defined circular orbits and they give no clue as to the exact whereabouts of the electron. This last problem had already bothered de Broglie very much and it had made physicists reluctant to accept his theory. De Broglie did not state therefore that an electron was a wave, but that he visualised the movement of an electron to be accompanied by a wave. Once the wave nature of electrons was established, however, this awkward question arose more forcibly. Where in the wave is the electron? Is it a little thing in the centre of the wave packet, or does it move around in the wave at random, or is it spread all over the wave? In fact are wave and electron the same thing?

For a time feeling ran high among physicists who held

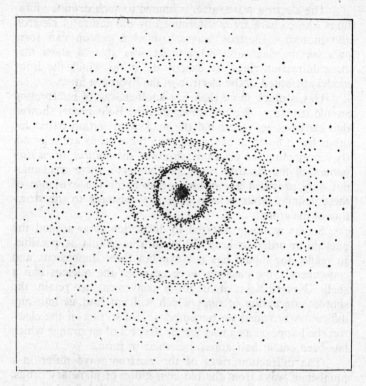

Fig. 18. *Quantum mechanics explains the electron orbits as diffraction rings of the electron waves round the nucleus.*

different views, but the controversy was cut short by a surprising and discouraging solution put forward by Heisenberg. He argued that there is little sense in talking about the exact position and speed of an electron unless we have a means of locating it. The exact position of a rifle bullet at a given time for instance, can be spotted with high speed photography. Of course, it is necessary to illuminate the bullet. In some such way one could imagine a method of determining the location of an electron, but it would be found that a dismal calamity awaits us. Each light quantum in the illumination has energy, and when one quantum encounters the electron, far from locating it, it will give it a push. If a less energetic quantum were chosen, being a light wave of longer wavelength, it would be too long to reveal the electron's position accurately. Heisenberg showed conclusively that the uncertainty which arises in this way in determining the position and speed of elementary particles has nothing to do with the particular kind of experiment employed, but that the dilemma is due to the nature of thinks and that it is inevitable.

Heisenberg's fundamental law has become known as the " principle of indeterminacy " and has provided ample food for discussion among physicists and particularly philosophers. If, they argue, the exact conditions of a physical system cannot be stated, then there is no point in expecting that these conditions will lead to a pre-determined result. The issue is of paramount importance and a furious debate began to rage over the conceptions of causality and free will. To some extent it still goes on, but fortunately we need not concern outselves too much since, as we shall presently see, the minds of physicists have more or less been set at rest.

Heisenberg's principle of indeterminacy put a stop to all further attempts at locating the electron within the confines of its de Broglie wave, but it did not solve the riddle of the wave itself. The question as to the physical nature of the de Broglie waves remained. Are they physical realities or mere mathematical figments? That they were real was strongly supported by the great success of Schrödinger's work, and for a time it seemed as if particles were indeed tangible vibrations in space the wavelength of which changes with the speed of the packet. Such a situation as this seemed odd, but so many odd conceptions had turned out to be realities of late that physicists were quite resigned to accept electrons which grew in extent as they moved more slowly, provided they kept together at all. This, however, they did not seem to do. Davisson and Germer and Sir George Thomson had photographed definite light *spots* in their diffraction experiments and, whatever one may expect of electrons, it seemed to be asking a lot of them that each should split up when passing through the sieve and that its parts should settle in different places. What, for instance, would become of its electric charge which, as is known, cannot be subdivided.

This and many other questions of a similar nature, and in fact the full physical significance of the matter waves, were cleared up by the brilliant interpretation of the quantum phenomena given by Born. Like all complete solutions of fundamental problems, it is astonishing in its simplicity.

Let us return for a moment to the crude experiment of passing a stream of sand through a sieve (p. 58). The number of grains arriving on a particular spot of the black cloth during a given time is determined by the chance of grains being scattered to this spot. In the centre of the cloth, directly underneath the stream, this chance is very great and we can confidently expect a great number of grains to fall here. Further away from the centre the probability that a grain will arrive is smaller, and there will come a region where it is most unlikely that a grain will come down. Nevertheless, it is still possible, though highly improbable, that a grain of sand will bounce off several times from the mesh and finally land far away from the centre. Thus it is the *probability* of grains being scattered into a particular direction which determines the aspect of the patch of sand under the sieve. One or two or even three single grains of sand dropped through the sieve can thus give us no clue as to the ultimate pattern of the patch.

The same line of reasoning was applied by Born to the diffraction pattern produced by electrons. The spots on the photographic plate (see plate IV) are not caused by electrons which have torn themselves to pieces, they mark those regions of the plate where electrons are most likely to arrive. A single electron passing through the sieve may arrive at any of the spots. There is a greater chance that it will land at a bright spot than at a weak one, but because of the principle of indeterminacy it is impossible to foretell definitely where it will strike the plate. The riddle of de Broglie's matter waves was solved; they are waves of probability.

With one stroke Born's interpretation solved innumerable difficulties. The peculiar diffuse rings which Schrödinger's diffraction pattern had substituted for Bohr's electron orbits acquired an entirely new meaning. They tell us how great the chance is of finding the electron in a particular spot. The denser the pattern is, the greater the probability of encountering the electron. The dense centres of the rings correspond to the old planetary orbits. Anywhere along these orbits the electron will be encountered with equal and high probability, while it is less likely to be found in the diffuse rims of the rings.

The dreadful calamity of indeterminacy is also avoided. It is true that, taking a single electron one cannot state its position more definitely than by the brightness of the diffraction ring, and one cannot exclude the possibility that it may be in a dim corner of the pattern instead of sailing along the densest part of the ring. This, however, is very unlikely and, taking not one but a million electrons, we can say almost with *certainty* that nearly all the electrons will be in the Bohr orbits, right in the centres of the rings.

The statistical character of quantum physics can be illustrated by an everyday example. In a large factory employing 1000 workers each worker will for some reason or other leave his bench for an average of about 6 minutes an hour. Thus if the manager were to go to any particular bench he woud stand a reasonable chance (10%) of finding it empty. The probability of finding *all* 1000 benches empty at the same time, however, is extremely remote (1/100,000 . . . thousand 0s).

The laws of probability see to it that an unlikely event becomes much more unlikely if a great number of instances is considered. It is, for example, unlikely that a man who sets out to found a family will eventually end up with, say, seven children all of whom are daughters. Nevertheless, everyone will have heard of such families. An unbroken string of seven daughters is admittedly improbable but not sufficiently unlikely for anyone to feel safe with regard to such an event. On the other hand, the chance that in London only girls will be born is so remote that it can be ruled out of the range of normal possibilities. In fact, population statistics happily proceed on the assumption that there will be as many boys born as girls.

Indeterminacy (of sex) rules the population aspect of the family ... but completely loses its importance when a larger unit—for instance a town —is considered.

Fig. 19. *Indeterminacy is the fundamental principle of quantum mechanics.*

A grain of sand contains many hundred million million million more electrons than greater London has inhabitants and the chance that all these electrons or even a noticeable fraction of them should be in odd improbable places at the same time can be completely discarded. The result is that, although the grain of sand or any other chunk of matter which we can perceive with our senses is built up of elementary particles that are subject to the principle of indeterminacy, there are always so many of them that we need not worry about the uncertainty of the continued safe existence of each grain of sand. It is true that we are condemned to remain forever vague and uncertain about the position of each elementary building brick in the structure of matter, but the laws of probability save us from being equally uncertain about the structure as a whole.

The relation of a single atom to the tiniest speck of dust, just visible under the most powerful microscope, is similar to that of a single family to the population of the globe. The electrons in our particular atom may momentarily be in improbable positions which differ from those of the average atom, but this would not affect the whole speck. The one family may have seven daughters but that will have no influence on the trend of population in the world. It simply means that a family contains too few persons to have applied to it with advantage the methods of statistics. Just as for an individual atom; there is a principle of indeterminacy (of sex) ruling the population aspect of each family, yet this same principle loses all significance once we consider the world, a nation, or even a single town. The laws of "classical" physics which mankind has developed through the experience of milleniums are statistical laws which do not bother about individual atoms and into which Heisenberg's principle of indeterminacy does not therefore enter. The boundaries within which this principle keeps the position and speed of a particle uncertain are determined by Planck's quantum constant. This constant is so small that, while it is of paramount importance in atomic dimensions, its effect has completely vanished in the world of human proportions.

Here, at last, have we found the clear distinction between our everyday world and the world of atoms. The reason why it is not permissible to treat an atom like a toy solar system or any mechanical model is, that such models are based on statistical rules and the atom is not. Our conceptions of the world are determined by the position man occupies in the universe, and our imagination must fail when we try to leave this position. Man's picture of the physical world and his views on causality would be entirely different if he were much larger or much smaller than he is.

Thus atoms may be compared with things we can grasp, but they will not be *like them*, for atoms are quantum structures and obey laws which must remain outside our comprehension because they are outside our experience. To our mind even the smallest thing is definitely either here or there, not like an electron in the atom which can never be found except within the vague limits of its wave of probability. Measured by the standard of human experience the quantum world is a strange and eerie place in which the idea of certainty does not exist; and, since our method of thinking is based on the concepts of certainty and causality, it is as well that the quantum world is confined to atomic dimensions.

This last statement, however, is not quite true. It is found that the wavepacket of a particle, giving the space in which the particle can be found with certainty, spreads out in size as the particle moves more slowly. Electrons circle around their nuclei with an enormous velocity, and atoms and molecules themselves rush about with incredible speed. The speed of the molecules in the air, for instance, is about 1,000 miles per hour! This speed of the molecules serves to define the temperature, and when a substance is cooled the speed of its molecules is diminished. By cooling things almost to the absolute zero of temperature (-273 degrees centigrade) the motion of their molecules can be slowed down

Fig. 20. *A QUANTUM INTRUDER IN THE DIMENSIONS OF " CLASSICAL " PHYSICS*

The odd behaviour of liquid helium.

so much that their wave packets become large enough to be noticed, and then the quantum world begins to intrude into our dimensions. A beaker filled with liquid helium—the only substance which does not freeze at this low temperature—will empty itself of its own accord, the liquid creeping over the rim and running down the outside of the beaker. Such a glimpse into the phantom world of quantum phenomena must appear disconcerting to anyone, and it is hardly surprising that physicists at first did not believe their eyes. It is as if the helium atoms called out to them mockingly: " Look, we are not billiard balls or marbles. We are wave-packets, and while we are most probably inside the beaker don't be too certain. You also have a sporting chance of seeing us outside! "

It may seem as if this long excursion into the quantum world had led us astray from the path which should bring us to the harnessing of atomic energy. Matter waves, holes in the vacuum and the principle of indeterminacy must appear as unreal dreams and idle speculations to those who expect the progress of science to be a conscious, purposeful quest for the taming and utilization of natural forces. However, it is well to remember that a few years ago every physicist would have laughed at the idea of making use of the energy locked up in atomic nuclei. Their knowledge of the structure and mechanism of atoms was not gained in the hope of turning it to the benefit or the destruction of mankind but merely to satisfy man's insatiable curiosity. Like explorers in an unknown land, scientists probed into the strange world of the atom for the sole purpose of filling up a vacant patch on the map of knowledge. When the discovery which led to the harnessing of atomic energy was made, it came as an unexpected windfall, but not as an accident. For, unless the atomic world of quanta had been explored, the discovery would have gone unnoticed, and would have been passed over because it would not have been understood.

It is an inherent feature of the methods of science that it cannot proceed by leaps and bounds, leaving large gaps in the map unfilled. Quantum phenomena, abstract as they may appear, provide the key for the understanding of atomic processes. The recognition and exploration of these phenomena and the development of wave-mechanics were the pre-requisites to the advent of atomic power.

A striking example of the fruitfulness of wave-mechanical conceptions is provided by the enigmatic phenomenon of radioactivity. The word *enigmatic* is used from the standpoint of classical physics which cannot explain at all why in a piece of radium *some* of the atoms should blow up. According to ordinary mechanics an atom can either be stable or not. In the first case it will never change and in the second case it will change without delay. A billiard ball placed on a level table will never of its own accord begin to move, because it is in a stable position. If the same ball is placed on an inclined table, and thus into an unstable position, it will roll down immediately. The nuclei of the radium atoms are all alike. Why then should one of them shoot out an alpha-particle within the next second while its neighbour may remain intact for many thousand years?

This apparently insoluble problem yields to the methods of wave-mechanics. The particles which form the nuclei, protons and neutrons, are confined in an energy trough just as the earth is held in an energy trough by the sun. This nuclear energy trough will become the most important item in our account, because confined in it is the energy which furnishes the power of the uranium bomb. As we shall see later, the walls of this trough are produced by an entirely new kind of force and have a shape rather like the crater of a volcano. The de Broglie waves of the particles forming the nucleus and lying within the trough penetrate to a certain extent into its walls. In ordinary atoms the de Broglie waves are completely confined by the thick walls. However, as one passes from lighter to heavier atoms with an ever increasing number of particles packed into the trough, a point will be reached when the waves begin to seep through the tapering walls.

This does not mean, of course, that one or more of the particles inside will immediately leave the nucleus and fly off. The de Broglie waves are, as we have seen, waves of probability, and when the fringes of the waves leak through the walls of the trough, it only means that the particles have

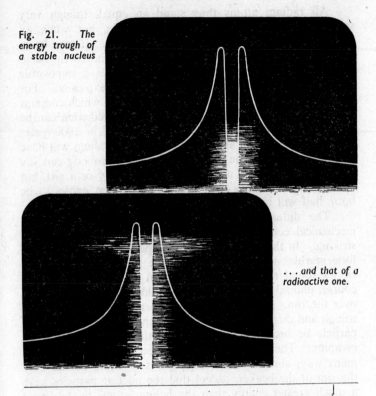

Fig. 21. The energy trough of a stable nucleus

... and that of a radioactive one.

a chance, however small, to be found *outside* the trough instead of inside it. In atoms, up to and including numbers 82 and 83 (Lead and Bismuth), the de Broglie waves of the nuclear particles are entirely confined to the inside of the energy trough, but in the last nine atoms (numbers 84-92, polonium to uranium) the fringes of the wavepackets reach through the trough's walls. The latter atoms are radioactive because, in a radium atom, to take one example, nuclear particles have a small but definite probability of escaping out of the nucleus. Why, when this event occurs, not a single proton or neutron should escape but an alpha-particle, consisting of two neutrons and two protons, is not fully clear, but this detail does not affect the general picture.

All radium atoms thus stand an equal, though very small, chance of loosing an alpha-particle, but when an individual atom will blow up we cannot say. It may be in the next instant, it may not happen for a hundred thousand years. The principle of indeterminacy makes it impossible to predict the time of the expected nuclear explosion. For a whole piece of radium, on the other hand, which contains an innumerable multitude of atoms, a safe prediction can be made. It can be stated with certainty that in 1600 years from now half of the atoms in any piece of radium will have blown up. It is again the same old story; nobody can say whether Mrs. Jones's next baby will be a boy or a girl, but it is quite safe to say that of the next million babies to be born, half will be boys.

The difference between the classical and the wave-mechanical conceptions of particles in an energy trough is striking. In the classical model the particles are pictured as little marbles whirling around in the trough. Each marble circles round rather like the earth in its orbit and it is, of course, unthinkable that it should suddenly leak out or jump over the rim. A marble can be either inside or outside the trough and there it will remain. It cannot like an elementary particle be inside and at the same time have a chance of escaping. The wave-mechanical aspect of radioactivity is in many ways similar to the leaking out of liquid helium over the rim of the beaker, except that the nuclear particles have a much greater energy than the helium atoms in the liquid and fly off with a high velocity, once they have escaped. Again the profound difference between the wave-mechanical and the classical aspects becomes apparent when the behaviour of a beaker of liquid helium is compared with that of a beaker filled with water.

If wave-mechanics had achieved nothing else but to show physicists a way out of the dilemma into which the discovery of radioactivity had brought them, it would have proved its worth. Its value, however, is far greater. Wave-mechanics was developed to provide an interpretation of the nature of the elementary particles, and achieved its first and greatest triumphs in the explanation of the behaviour of the electron cloud outside the nucleus. So much more is known about the outer regions of the atom than about the nucleus, and consequently the all important concepts of wave-mechanics had first to be based on and checked against observations on the electron cloud, before they could be applied to the problems of the nucleus and the release of atomic energy.

CHAPTER SIX

THE diameter of the atomic nucleus is about 10,000 times smaller than the diameter of the whole atom. Quantum mechanics which, as we have seen, plays such an important part in the structure of the electron cloud assumes an even greater importance in the sub-atomic space of the nucleus. When in 1911 Rutherford proposed his model of the atom, consisting of a nucleus with an enveloping electronic cloud, the composition of the nucleus appeared to present little difficulty. At that time the importance of the quantum principle had hardly been realised, and it is significant that the original conception of nuclear structure, based as it was on classical physics, had ultimately to be discarded in favour of a quantum model in spite of the fact that the classical model of the nucleus seemed to be in admirable agreement with the observed phenomena.

Until 1919 when Rutherford carried out the first artificial transmutation, all information about the composition of the atomic nuclei rested on the observations of radiations emanating from the radioactive elements. It was soon recognised that these radiations have their source in the nuclei about whose structure they provide information just as light waves and x-rays reveal the structure of the electronic cloud. In the early experiments on radium three different kinds of rays were discovered which Rutherford called alpha-, beta- and gamma-rays. Only the gamma-rays turned out to be electromagnetic waves like those of light, while the alpha-rays, as we already know, are positively charged helium nuclei (alpha-particles) which are shot out of radium nuclei with immense speed. The beta-rays, too, are projectiles; they are negatively charged electrons (plate V). Rutherford's bombardment of nitrogen with alpha-particles produced finally a fourth type of nuclear radiation in the form of protons. Since electrons and protons are the elementary particles blown out when a nucleus disintegrates, it is natural to assume, indeed it appears inevitable, that they live within the nucleus before the catastrophy of disintegration overtakes them. The components of a bomb can be gauged by the debris which it casts about and for a long time it was thought that nuclei are made up of protons and electrons only. The helium nucleus, for example, which has the weight 4 was believed to consist of 4 positive protons and 2 negative electrons, giving it a net charge of $+2$.

All this seemed to be in satisfactory agreement with the observations. The positive protons were thought to be held together by the presence of the negative electrons which owing to their insignificant mass would not contribute appreciably to the weight of the nucleus. However, when attempts were made to describe this nuclear model in greater detail by accurate calculation, a disconcerting fact came to light. It was shown that the energy of motion of the electrons, confined in the small space of the nucleus and in close proximity to the protons, would have to be very great. In fact, it would be so great that any electron in the nucleus would break away at once, like a stone which is whirled around too violently on a weak string. At first, of course, scientists were reluctant to scrap an otherwise satisfactory theory and the result of the calculation was checked again and again. There was little doubt however; it was correct. Moreover, from other observations, evidence began to accumulate which could not be reconciled with the presence of electrons in the nucleus.

Realisation of the fact that there are no electrons inside the nucleus not only demolished the one nuclear model which appeared feasible at the time, but it also brought in its trail a host of most awkward questions. Since, except for hydrogen, all nuclei contain more units of weight than units of positive charge, protons alone cannot account for all the mass. How then was the extra mass of the nucleus made up? It was also clear that, whatever the contents of the nucleus might be, it is positively charged. What held this positively charged nucleus together, if not electrons, the only negative particles known? Above all, observation had shown beyond any shadow of doubt that radioactive nuclei ejected electrons in the form of beta-rays. Whence could these electrons have come, if not out of the nucleus? While the damage to the original nuclear model was beyond repair, it became immediately clear that in order to build up a new and better one, a new kind of brick and a new kind of mortar would be needed. Where and how were they to be found?

As early as 1920 Rutherford suggested that there may exist yet another elementary building brick in addition to the proton and the electron, a new kind of particle which differed from the known ones by the fact that it has no electric charge. This lack of charge he said would be the reason why such a particle, although it may exist in abundance, had escaped notice. An electrically charged particle like a proton or an electron, when it escapes from the nucleus and passes through air, will tear off some of the outer electrons of the air molecules which stand in its way, like a man who rushes through a crowd will leave in his wake parcels, umbrellas and walking sticks which he has knocked out of the hands of the bystanders. This ability to produce charged air molecules is used by nuclear physicists to observe alpha- and beta-rays, and in an ingenious apparatus devised by C. T. R. Wilson of Cambridge, called the cloud chamber, the tracks of particles can actually be made visible like vapour trails left by high flying aircraft (see plate IX). A neutral particle on the other hand will pass through the electronic clouds of other atoms or molecules as easily as a knife through butter. It will not be deflected. The only hope of detecting such a particle lies in the rare chance of a direct collision with a nucleus when it may cause this nucleus to recoil or break up.

Ten years after Rutherford's suggestion, two German scientists, Bothe and Becker, observed what they thought were extremely powerful gamma-rays which made their appearance when the elements lithium, beryllium and boron were subjected to a bombardment with alpha-particles. The mystery deepened when the Curie-Joliots found that, while these rays could penetrate thick shields of lead, they were easily stopped by paraffin wax, a substance which is known to let through gamma-rays. The riddle was solved in 1932 by Sir James Chadwick who showed that the new radiation was a stream of uncharged particles, namely neutrons, which were expelled from the bombarded nuclei when the latter were hit by alpha-particles. In the following year the existence of these neutrons was confirmed by Feather in Cambridge who observed atomic vapour trails which appeared to start without cause (plate VI). These were recoil tracks of atoms hit by neutrons which, of course, had left no trails themselves.

The discovery of the neutron provided physicists with the much needed new building brick for the structure of the nucleus. There remained, however, the question of the mortar. Neutrons clearly came out of bombarded nuclei and it could safely be assumed therefore that the mass of all atomic nuclei is made up of protons and neutrons. But this does not yet explain how the nucleus is kept together. The two neutrons in a helium nucleus, for example, cannot be expected to hold the two protons in check by their mere presence. The protons, being positively charged, instead of sticking to each other as they quite evidently do, should repel one another violently. Gravitational attraction, the only force which our experience allots to an uncharged particle, is far too small in nuclear particles to overcome the strong electrical repulsion of the protons. Scientists were thus faced with the dilemma that apart from a new particle, something entirely new was also required in the way of forces to hold particles together. These new forces evidently would make their appearance only in the submicroscopic world of atomic dimensions, since all phenomena in the large scale world as it appears to our senses can be explained by the attraction of gravity or the attraction and repulsion of electricity and magnetism.

The fact that the force binding the nucleus together is confined to the dimensions of the atom is a sure pointer to its origin; it must be a quantum-mechanical effect. Quite some time before the difficulties in the explanation of nuclear structure became evident, much the same situation had arisen with regard to the structure of the molecules.

The formation of chemical compounds from different elements is associated with quite considerable energy changes. For instance the combination of carbon and oxygen, resulting in the formation of carbon dioxide, a process commonly known as the burning of coal, provides mankind with the power that at present keeps our industries going. It is evident from this fact that some strong forces must act between the oxygen and the carbon atom. From what has been said in earlier chapters about the structure of atoms, however, one would hardly expect an attraction between these atoms. On the contrary, the electronic clouds of both atoms bear negative electric charges and when the atoms are brought into close proximity to each other, far from being bound to one another, they should repel each other. For some time it was supposed that one kind of atom would take away one or more electrons from the other kind, and that the two different atoms would then have opposing electric charges which would, by their attraction, keep the atoms held together. This explanation sufficed for want of anything better, but it was not very convincing because no satisfactory reason could be given why one atom should capture the other's electrons. Moreover the situation became quite hopeless when one attempted to explain in the same manner the existence of, for example, a hydrogen molecule which consists of two *identical* atoms; and scientists were at a still greater loss when trying to account for the very strong forces holding together a piece of iron, consisting as it does entirely of atoms of the same kind.

As was to be expected, chemical binding forces turned out to be a pure quantum effect, and the provision of a full and satisfactory explanation for these and similar forces was probably the greatest achievement of quantum mechanics. Quantum mechanical considerations showed that a strong force will bind two atoms together when they share one or more electrons between them. Unfortunately, there exists no analogy in classical physics by which this "exchange phenomenon," as it is called, can be compared with happenings in the sphere of human experience. Exchange forces arise from the fact that quantum mechanics always associates a characteristic vibration with any energy change, an instance of this occurs in the jump of an electron from one orbit to another which gives rise to a light wave of a certain definite colour. For the benefit of the mathematically minded an

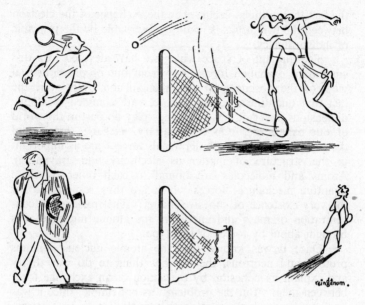

Fig. 22. *Exchange attraction.*

exchange force can be compared with the exchange of the modes of oscillation between two loosely coupled pendulums, but for those who do not appreciate the analogy in its mathematical formalism, this comparison will remain empty and void of meaning. As has been said before, it is in the nature of quantum mechanical explanations that they never allow satisfactory analogies, and a proper understanding of the mechanism of exchange forces must rest on their mathematical interpretation. Alternatively, those who are prepared to sacrifice the physical meaning of the phenomenon to an easy, though vague, interpretation, can compare two identical atoms sharing an electron with two tennis players who determine each other's action by continually exchanging the ball in play. As long as the ball moves between them, their mutual interest in it draws the players together, but they are free to part as soon as the game is finished. How inadequate such a comparison must necessarily remain is emphasized by the fact that in the molecule even the exchange of the electron between the two atoms is made unobservable by the principle of indeterminacy.

The amount of space which we have devoted to a discussion of exchange forces may seem out of proportion in view of the obscurity of the phenomenon. However, the fact that quantum mechanical forces are confined to atomic dimensions does not mean that they play no part in the world of our experience. On the contrary, exchange forces and their companions, the van der Waals forces* are as important in the structure of matter as electricity and gravitation. Atoms and molecules are bound to each other by these quantum mechanical forces which are thus responsible for the very existence of cohesive matter. The tremendous concentration of mass and energy in the atomic nuclei, too, is brought about by forces of this type.

Once it was known that the atomic nucleus contains protons and neutrons, the obvious thing to do was to try and explain its cohesion by the action of an exchange force between them. But the problem was not simple, since it was known that the exchanged particle could not be an electron. It was indeed this very fact that electrons cannot be kept inside the nucleus which had led to the overthrow of Rutherford's original nuclear model. The solution of this problem is linked with one of the strangest stories in the history of nuclear research.

In 1934 a Japanese physicist, Yukawa, calculated on the basis of available data the probable exchange forces in atomic nuclei and he came to the conclusion that protons and neutrons can only be held together if they share a negatively charged particle, having the same charge as an electron but with about 150 times the electron's mass. Yukawa's invention of such a particle, which was not known to exist, solely for the purpose of providing the right kind of mortar for the bricks of the nucleus, was considered rather artificial and

---

* When two atoms come close together, the outer electrons begin to move in unison, just as a tuning fork can set another one in vibration. This "resonance" of the outer electrons produces an attraction, the van der Waals force, between the atoms. The van der Waals forces are responsible for the cohesion of all substances except metals. The cohesion of metals is due to exchange forces.

little notice was taken of his work. Two years later, however, physicists engaged on the observation of cosmic rays, the strange radiation which had previously led to the discovery of positive electrons, noticed a peculiar type of track. The track was caused by a heavy negative particle which had only a short lifetime and which subsequently disintegrated. Closer examination showed that this "heavy electron" had exactly the properties of Yukawa's hypothetical particle, and it was only then that his work was remembered. The existence of this new particle, called the meson (plate VI) is to-day established beyond doubt, and while it is still too early to state definitely whether the strong cohesion of atomic nuclei is due to the exchange of mesons between protons and neutrons, the evidence for it is strong.

It is a characteristic feature of exchange forces that they act only over a very short distance. We and all things around us are bound to this earth by the force of gravity, and it is this same force which keeps the moon in its orbit around the earth and the earth revolving around the sun. As Newton first showed, and as every schoolchild knows to-day, the force of gravity diminishes inversely as the square of the distance between the gravitating masses. This means, that if by some cosmic miracle the distance between earth and moon were to be increased to twice its present length, the force between them would drop to 1/4 of its original strength. Taking the moon away to three times its present distance would lower the mutual attraction to 1/9, and so on. The same law holds for the attraction and repulsion of electric charges. The strength of an exchange force, on the other hand, decreases much more rapidly with increasing distance. When the distance between two particles is doubled, the exchange force falls to much less than a quarter of its original value. Hence, whereas the forces of gravity and electricity die off gradually with growing distance and are capable of holding together bodies at distances much greater than atomic dimensions, exchange forces are extremely strong, outweighing all other forces, so long as the particles are close together, but they rapidly become negligible with increasing distance. The range of exchange forces does not reach out beyond the atomic world.

The nature of nuclear exchange forces immediately provides an explanation for the existence and the greatness of atomic energy. A number of protons, all positively charged, repel each other with considerable force and this repulsion grows as the distance between them is diminished, fourfold when the distance is halved, ninefold when it is reduced to a third. The attraction of an exchange force, however, grows still more rapidly as the distance is reduced so that at a sufficiently small distance the electric repulsion between the protons, however great, will be overbalanced by the still greater exchange attraction. The distance at which this happens determines the size of the atomic nucleus. In order to remain together, the protons in the nucleus must be in close proximity. Once one or more of them are taken out of the reach of the exchange forces, they will escape, never to return; the nucleus will disintegrate. Furthermore, when a proton is taken beyond the range of the exchange forces, the strong electrical repulsion acting, no longer counterbalanced, will make itself felt and the proton will be shot out of the nucleus with immense speed. Atomic energy is liberated.

Thus the difference between the relative sizes of the nucleus and the atom as a whole, mentioned at the beginning of this chapter, contains the reason for the striking difference between atomic and ordinary chemical energy. In a chemical reaction one or more electrons are detached from the periphery of the atom while in a nuclear transmutation one or more protons are taken out of the nucleus. Both electron and proton have unit electric charges, but the force acting between the proton and the other nuclear particles is more than a hundred million times stronger than the force acting on the electron. This is because inside the nucleus the particles are so very much closer to each other than the outer electrons are to the nucleus. Figures with many noughts mean little but it may help to visualise atomic proportions when we remember that the distance between two nuclear particles compares with that of the outer electron as the width of a street to the distance London-Rome. The forces acting on a proton and on one of the electrons can be compared with the noise of an alarm clock on the bedside table and one that is more than fifty miles away!

So far only attractive forces between one proton and one neutron have been mentioned. However the very existence and the strong cohesion of nuclei containing a number of protons and a number of neutrons, make it clear that in the nucleus there is not just a bond between two individual particles but between several of them. A striking example of this is provided by the alpha-particle in which 2 protons and 2 neutrons are so closely united that even in so cataclysmic an event as the disintegration of a radium atom these four elementary particles remain together and are ejected as a whole from the nucleus. The fact that all alpha-particles shot out of disintegrating nuclei of different elements are alike, consisting always of 2 protons and 2 neutrons, gives them an appearance analogous to that of molecules of a chemical compound.

In a crude analogy we can liken two particles held together by exchange forces to two bar magnets attracting one another. The force between the magnets resembles that between two nuclear particles because it is of relatively short reach. Two bar magnets suspended close together will

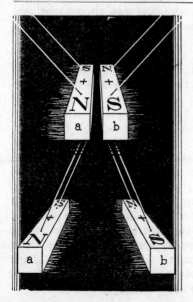

Fig. 23. *The force between two electrically charged bar magnets resembles to some extent the force acting between two protons in an atomic nucleus. The magnets will attract each other when they are close together but repel each other when they are separated.*

attract each other strongly because their opposite poles are near one another. In Fig. 23 the north pole of magnet *a* is strongly attracted by the south pole of magnet *b* which is in its immediate vicinity. On the other hand, the north pole of *a* will suffer only a weak repulsion from the north pole of *b*, because the latter is kept at a distance by the length of the magnet. The same argument holds for the forces acting on the opposite end of the magnet *a* and thus the net effect is a strong attraction between the two magnets. The situation is, however, quite different when the two magnets are separated by a distance which is large in comparison with their length. Now the north pole of *a* is almost as far away from the south pole of *b* as from the north pole of *b*. Therefore the attraction which the north pole of *a* experiences from the south pole of *b* will be practically balanced out by the repulsion which it suffers from the north pole of *b*. As a result the attraction between the two magnets will be negligible.

Crude as this model is, we can go further and simulate even more closely the forces between two protons in a nucleus by supplying the two bar magnets with positive electric charges. Charges of similar electrical sign always repel one another, but when the magnets are close together this repulsion is more than balanced out by the magnetic attraction. If, however, the magnets are at a distance this attractive force is, as we have just seen, extremely small, and they will now be pushed apart strongly by the action between their positive electric charges.

This little model, while it cannot reflect the true physical character of the quantum-mechanical force, will help us to understand the peculiar shape of the nuclear energy trough. Earlier in our account we have encountered the funnel-shaped energy trough created by the gravitational attraction of the sun around which trough the planets move, and the step-like trough in which electrons are confined by the attraction of the nucleus in an atom. Later, when discussing the nature of radioactive processes it was stated that nuclear particles, too, live in such an energy trough the shape of which was compared with that of a volcano. (Figure 21). This shape can now be explained in terms of short range attractive forces and long range repulsive forces.

In the spontaneous disintegration of radioactive nuclei and in many artificial transmutations alpha-particles are ejected. These alpha-particles are positively charged and could not be kept in the nucleus at all if it were not for the exchange forces of short range which bind them to the rest of the nucleus. Let us see what will happen in a stable nucleus, that is one which is not radioactive, if sufficient energy is supplied to pull an alpha-particle out of it. The only way to remove an alpha-particle from its nuclear trough is to lift it up along the inside wall. The great height and steepness of this inner wall is created by the attraction of the exchange forces. If the particle is given sufficient energy to overcome this attraction, in other words if it is lifted to the top of the inside wall of the trough, it will find itself on the rim of the crater where at the slightest push it can either fall back into the trough or roll down the outer slope. This point indicates the place at which the electric force of repulsion just balances the exchange force of attraction. Here no net force at all acts on the particle. In real fact the arrival of a particle at the rim of the crater is a very unlikely state of affairs. We have seen in an earlier chapter that nuclear particles because of their quantum nature do not behave like marbles is an ordinary trough. On the contrary, if the alpha-particle is lifted to a sufficient height inside the crater, it can seep through the wall and escape. The chance of doing this increases the nearer the particle approaches the rim. Whether the alpha-particle is actually lifted over the rim or whether it leaks through, it will roll down the outer slope, gathering speed all the time. This outer slope is produced by the long range repulsive force due to the positive charges of nucleus and particle. Thus the alpha-particle comes out of the disturbed nucleus with a speed depending on the height of the slope.

Since atoms of the same element all have the same kind of energy trough, alpha-particles escaping from them will all roll down the same slope. In other words, the alpha-particles should all escape with the same energy. This has actually been found to be true. Photographs of the tracks of alpha-particles emanating from a piece of radium show that these tracks have all the same length (plate V).

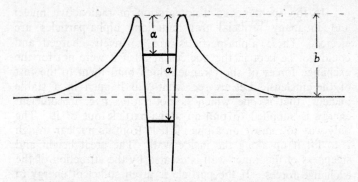

Fig. 24. *In order to remove an alpha-particle or a proton from the nuclear energy trough it has to be lifted through the distance (a) and will then roll down the slope (b). Thus (a) is the energy which must be supplied and (b) is the energy gained. If (b) is greater than (a), the reaction as a whole will yield energy. This simplified picture takes no account of the fact that, because of the quantum nature of the process, the particle stands a certain chance of escaping from the trough without energy being supplied. This chance is only appreciable if the particle occupies an energy level near the rim of the trough.*

In the same way as the energy imparted to the escaping particle is determined by the height of the outer slope down which it runs, the energy put into the nucleus to cause its escape is measured by the height to which the particle must be lifted in order to reach the rim. If this latter height is greater than the height of the slope, the process taken as a whole consumes more energy than it gives out, since more work has to be expended in lifting the particle inside the crater than can be gained in the drop outside. On the other hand, if the particle were originally inside the nucleus at a level higher than that of the outside plain, the reaction will result in a net evolution of energy. Thus a nucleus containing an alpha-particle at a high level constitutes an energy store of atomic dimensions. Work can be drawn from it, just as work can be obtained from a water reservoir containing water at a level higher than that outside. If a method can be devised by which each individual nucleus is given just the necessary amount of energy to unlock its energy store, atomic energy can be utilised on a scale suitable for power production.

Imagine a man standing on the dam of a water reservoir and scooping water out with a bucket into a shoot which runs down the outside of the dam. At the bottom of the shoot there is a turbine in which the water is made to do work, for example by driving a dynamo. This man has to do a certain amount of work to lift water out of the reservoir; but, because of the greater drop, the same amount of water will do more work in the turbine than that necessary to draw it up from the reservoir. If the man is now replaced by an electromotor which is fed from the dynamo, the whole process will be self-sustaining. The dynamo will not only supply sufficient current to drive the motor; it will have also plenty of electric power to spare which can be put to productive use. By applying this picture to the atomic nucleus we see that if some of the energy gained by the particle rolling down the slope can be used to liberate a particle in another nucleus, a self sustaining nuclear reaction would be achieved. In such a "chain reaction" the enormous energy store of atomic nuclei could be triggered off.

One of the most important details to find out is clearly the heights of the levels at which the particles live in the nuclear craters. It would appear from our picture that nuclei containing many particles should be the most likely to yield energy-producing reactions, since their craters are filled to a high level. To a certain extent this is so and this argument of a highly filled nuclear trough has already been used to explain the behaviour of radioactive nuclei. In these it was assumed, the crater is filled to such a high level that alpha-particles are able to seep through the rim. Atoms like these must be unstable; they must break up sooner or later by disgorging a particle. While our argument can be applied to radioactivity, it is nevertheless faulty in a number of ways. Instability is not solely a result of the packing of a great number of particles into the trough. Experiments have shown that nuclei which contain only a small number of particles may be unstable too. In fact, according to the present views on nuclear reactions the "splitting" of an atom by bombardment is not an instantaneous process; instead the bombarding particle entering the nucleus remains there for a little while. The new nucleus thus formed, although it may contain only a few particles, turns out to be unstable and throws out a particle, thereby relapsing into a stable form.

What nuclear physicists are, of course, aiming at is a full theory of atomic nuclei from which the distribution of energy levels in each individual nuclear trough can be predicted by calculation. If all the forces acting within a physical system are known it must in principle be possible to predict the state of this system at any future time. The solar system can serve as an example. Since Copernicus, Kepler and Newton, astronomers have been able to calculate in advance the constellations of the planets and their satellites with a high degree of accuracy. The Newtonian theory of gravitation, rigorously applied to the observed movement of the planet Uranus led to the discovery—by calculation—of a new planet, Neptune. Thus there are two different elements, not always sharply divided, which enter into any exact interpretation of a natural phenomenon; knowledge of the nature of the physical forces involved and their mathematical description. Newton's law for the force acting between two heavy bodies is supremely simple, but as soon as a third, a fourth or a fifth body is introduced the problem becomes very complicated. This complication is due, not to the appearance of any new physical forces, gravitation remains the only force to be considered, but purely to mathematical difficulties. While there exists a simple equation for the forces between two bodies, no such equation can be written down for the forces between three or more bodies and the mathematical calculations consequently can only be made by approximation. The great success of early astronomers in describing with fair accuracy the movements of planets can be attributed to the overriding influence of the sun in the solar system. The total mass of the planets and their satellites amounts to no more than to 1.5% of the mass of the sun, and in consequence, except for some very insignificant corrections, the sun alone determines the shape and depth of the solar energy trough. This makes things easy from the mathematical point of view. In an atomic nucleus, on the other hand, there are a number of particles of equal size all of which exert forces upon each other. Their movements are not governed, as those of the planets, by a central body. This is just the kind of problem which is very difficult to solve. Moreover, while it appears that the mutual electric repulsion of protons obeys the simple inverse square law even in the narrow confines of the nucleus, little is known about the nature and behaviour of the attractive forces acting. As was pointed out before, at the present time physicists are inclined to attribute this attraction force to the exchange of mesons, but there is much disagreement concerning the exact mechanism of this exchange.

The atomic nucleus is not the first case in which physicists have been confronted with the problem of a number of particles which exert roughly equal forces upon each other. For example, in the agglomeration of a number of atoms to form a molecule, that is in the formation of a chemical compound, the atoms very often are of almost equal mass, just as protons and neutrons inside a nucleus bear equal masses. Another example which possibly bears a still greater resemblance to an atomic nucleus is presented by a drop of liquid, which is built up of atoms all of the same size. Both these comparisons have indeed been used by scientists in their efforts to elucidate the nature of atomic nuclei and the latter in particular has met with considerable success. This " liquid drop theory " has helped much in the understanding of the process of nuclear fission which has made the release of atomic energy possible and which we shall discuss later in some detail. There is some reason to believe that the nuclear particles, like atoms in a drop of liquid, are not bound to fixed places or to definite orbits but move around at random. But there is also some evidence for a more ordered structure, like that of a molecule, in which the different atoms occupy more or less fixed positions. In this respect the fact that in so many nuclear reactions alpha-particles make their appearance seems to indicate that the four particles concerned stick together just as certain groups of atoms often appear together in the formation of chemical compounds. It has for instance been suggested that an oxygen nucleus of mass 16 may be built up of four alpha-particles which are arranged in a simple geometrical pattern. However, these analogies though they are used by physicists themselves, and though they are admittedly on a somewhat higher level than the crude comparisons with roundabouts and tennis players, have also to be taken with a grain of salt. The physicist does not really mean that an atomic nucleus looks like a molecule or a drop of water. At most he means that the same methods which have proved useful in the description of a molecule or of a droplet may be likely to be of use also in the interpretation of the nucleus.

Thus while scientists have learned a good deal about the composition and nature of the atomic nucleus, much more remains to be discovered. A satisfactory explanation of the atom's central core cannot be given until all the essential facts have been marshalled and at present it seems that there remains much which is hidden. Nuclear physics is still at the stage where the experiment leads and theory follows. It is true that of late a number of theoretical predictions by Bohr and his co-workers have inspired experimental work and were confirmed through it. But instances like these are rather the exception than the rule. All the time new and unsuspected facts concerning the nuclear particles are being discovered and a thorough theory of the nucleus will have to wait until this flood of novel facts has subsided.

Even so, as we have seen, a rough picture of the nucleus can be obtained at the present stage. For instance, experiments have thrown light on the question why the number of existing nuclei is limited. This account began by stating that there are 92 different elements, that is 92 different kinds of atoms. Later it was explained that the actual number of different nuclei is somewhat greater because an element may have a number of isotopes. Isotopes, it will be recalled, are atoms containing the same number of protons and consequently the same number of electrons in their electronic clouds but with different numbers of neutrons in their nuclei. However, not all elements have been found to have isotopes and even those which do, only have a small number. It is only natural that one should wonder whether there may not exist many more nuclei made up in proportions of protons and neutrons other than those generally known. Take for example the element phosphorus. Its nucleus has the weight 31 and contains 15 protons and 16 neutrons. It is therefore described by the symbol $^{31}_{15}P$. Why then are there no nuclei with 15 protons but, let us say, 17 neutrons or 15 neutrons? To this question experiments have given an answer. These nuclei $^{32}_{15}$P and $^{30}_{15}$P can actually be made in the laboratory by bombardment. By shooting an alpha-particle into an aluminium nucleus a phosphorous atom with 15 neutrons can be created and by bombarding sulphur with neutrons, a phosphorous atom with 17 neutrons can be made. But then comes the snag. Neither of these artificially created isotopes of phosphorous will last for long. Like radium atoms, the newly made nuclei disintegrate spontaneously; they are unstable. It is significant what happens to them. The nucleus $^{32}_{15}$P, which in comparison with ordinary phosphorous ($^{31}_{15}$P) has too high a proportion of neutrons, emits an electron and becomes sulphur, $^{32}_{16}$S. By getting rid of one negative charge in the form of an electron, the nucleus regains a proper balance between protons and neutrons. The other artificially created isotope of Phosphorous, $^{30}_{15}$P, which has too high a proportion of protons, also emits an electron. But in this case, it is a positive electron and the nucleus changes into a silicon atom, $^{30}_{14}$Si. Our question is thus answered, nuclei with other proportions of protons to neutrons than those which we meet with in the minerals of the earth's crust do not exist because they are unstable. If they are made artificially they will in a short time change on their own account into one of the familiar nuclei. In recent years an enormous number of such unstable nuclei have been made in the laboratory. More than 250 are known at present.

This artificial radioactivity has brought us back to one important problem for which no solution has so far been provided, namely the emission of electrons from the nucleus. We have populated the nucleus with protons, neutrons and mesons and we have seen that electrons cannot exist in it. Where therefore does an emitted electron come from? A clue to this riddle is provided by observations on cosmic rays. In many experiments, mesons have actually been observed and it has been found also that these free mesons are not stable particles; they, too, disintegrate. When a meson breaks up, an electron appears. The meson, it will be recalled, is a particle with the same unit negative charge as the electron but with greater mass. When it is transformed it is supposed to

break up into an electron and a neutrino. The neutrino is a
new particle which, like the neutron, has no charge but which
has a very small mass. Up to now, no one has been able to
observe this new particle which has been " invented " in order
to explain the disintegration of mesons and a number of other
nuclear changes.

Within the nucleus, mesons are exchanged between protons and neutrons. If a neutron gives away its meson to a
proton, it must change its nature, having parted with a unit
negative charge. It turns into a proton while the proton
taking up the negatively charged meson becomes a neutron.
Thus individual protons and neutrons continually interchange
their identity but the total number of neutrons and total number of protons remains the same. The proton-neutron pair
behave rather like our tennis players who also continually
change their roles, in this case between that of the active and
that of the passive partner. It has lately been found that

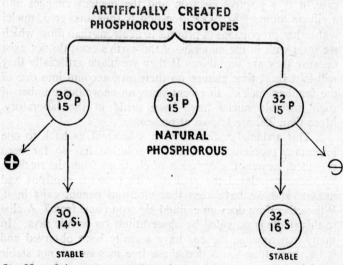

Fig. 25.   *Only certain proportions of protons and neutrons will yield stable
nuclei.   The stable phosphorus isotope $^{31}_{15}P$ contains 15 protons and 16 neutrons.
Phosphorus nuclei with 15 or 17 neutrons can be created artificially, but they
are unstable and decay after a short time.*

there exist not only negative but also positive mesons and we can think in the same way of protons parting with positive mesons and turning into neutrons, the receiving neutrons thereby becoming protons.

Since a meson passing through space disintegrates into an electron and a neutrino, the same may happen to a meson inside a nucleus. The electron produced in this way cannot be held by the nucleus because of its high energy of motion, and so it escapes. Here therefore is the solution to the riddle of the beta-rays. They are electrons which are born when a meson dies and which leave the nucleus at the moment of their birth. The decay of a positive meson will produce a positive electron.

In unravelling the story of the atomic nucleus we have come across a bewildering multitude of new particles. There was first the positive electron and then the mesons, negative and positive, and then the neutrino; and this may not be the end yet. Even if there are no further particles in store, our earlier statement that matter is composed of protons, neutrons and electrons, with which we began this book, must now appear somewhat weak. However, things are not quite as bad as they appear. We stand at the threshold of an entirely new conception concerning the nature of things. Slowly we begin to realise that matter and radiation in all their various aspects are but different forms of energy, the only content of the universe. The deeper we probe into the depth of space and into the minute cosmos of the atomic world, the more we are aware of the continual changing of energy from one form into the other. It appears that in these changes some particles, like the proton, the neutron and the electron, are the more permanent forms while others, like the mesons, the positive electrons and the neutrino, are short lived transient stages. One may even go a step further and regard the proton and the neutron as essentially one and the same particle to which the transient form of a positive or negative meson merely lends a particular aspect.

CHAPTER SEVEN

MASS INTO SUNSHINE

LESS than 350 years ago Giordano Bruno was burnt because he refused to believe that man occupied the centre of the universe. Since then our ideas have changed a good deal and it has become the fashion to admit humbly that we live in a most insignificant corner of the interstellar space. However, of late it has been realised that in spite of the very subordinate place to which this world of ours has been relegated by the efforts of astronomers. it is quite exceptional. It may well be that we inhabit one of the exceedingly rare pieces of solid matter which recur only at intervals of many billion miles. On this odd and unrepresentative place, this solid crust of the earth, man has developed his ideas about the nature of the physical world and it is not surprising therefore, that these ideas are equally odd and unrepresentative. To our mind changes occuring in atomic nuclei are strange and extremely rare events. It is only a mere fifty years ago, when scientists had developed delicate methods of detecting rays, that they discovered radioactivity, and that almost by accident. The slight blackening of a photographic plate was all the evidence which our world offered as a testimony to the most important physical process in the whole universe.

Atomic nuclei on earth are all carefully wrapped in their protective electronic clouds and never come into contact with each other. If it were not for the few radioactive atoms, left to us from a former period of stellar evolution, we would not know what nuclear reactions are. But such an arrangement of protected nuclei is not the normal state of matter in the universe at large. As far as we know it is a rare exception. In the sun and the stars nuclei are shorn of their electronic wrappers and they continually undergo reactions, releasing atomic energy on a more extensive scale than man fortunately has been able to achieve so far. Transmutation of the elements is the source of power inside the sun and in nearly all the stars, keeping them shining for millions of years to come. The atomic furnaces of the sun and stars on the whole burn steadily which, as far as life on this planet is concerned, must be regarded with satisfaction. Even so there are stars which flare up and explode providing on a gigantic and awe-inspring scale ample evidence of naturally created atomic bombs.

Although there are many stars more than 5000 times brighter than the sun and still more considerably weaker brothers, the sun itself is a tolerably normal member of the stellar famliy and, with the advantage of being close at hand to make observations easy, it makes an ideal specimen to be studied. The question of what makes it shine has troubled scientists for a number of centuries. What, so they asked, provides the prodigious quantity of light and heat, equivalent in output to an engine of 500,000 trillion horsepower. that it has poured out for millions of years past and which, barring accidents, it will continue to do for thousands of years to come? Naturally the first suggestion to make, based on experience of everyday life, is that it is a burning lump of coal of gigantic size. This somewhat naif idea is, however, quite absurd. If it were true, the sun would die away in a mere 8,000 years, a much smaller length of time than man's existence on the earth. To be any use, theory must show that the sun's life is at least as long as the estimated age of the oldest rocks found in the earth's crust; and from an estimate of the amount of radium and uranium left in these, we assume them to be about 2,000 million years old.

The next theory had a somewhat more scientific trend, but nevertheless it is equally absurd. Since the sun is a ball of gas it will, in the absence of other forces, shrink slowly and steadily in size, pulled inward upon itself by its own gravitational attraction. When a stone falls towards the centre of the earth, it loses potential energy, which can be turned into work; and so the sun in contracting must also give out energy. Kelvin and Helmholtz calculated that to account by gravity for its present ratiative powers, the sun must collapse at the rate of 9 inches every day. Though this seems to be little compared with the huge size of the sun, contraction at this rate would make it last for only about 30 million years, again not nearly enough to account even for the existence of its planets.

This problem of the sun and stars was only solved by the discovery of atomic energy. Just as in radium atoms break up and cause bits and pieces of subatomic size to fly off with enormous energy, so in the sun nuclear reactions must take place. A stick of dynamite, for example, besides sending debris flying far and wide, gives out a brilliant flash of light as it explodes; and so an atom, when it is transmuted, gives out a flash of gamma-rays. These rays as well as the sub-atomic particles that are ejected help to stoke the atomic fires in the sun's innermost core.

Radiation is, as we have seen one particular form of energy, and energy in turn is equivalent to mass. When a negative and a positive electron meet, their mass is annihilated and the energy released travels forth in the form of a gamma-ray. In making the energy for a flash, therefore, mass must be lost, and an atom by sending out a gamma-ray must become less in weight. This is a universal law applicable to light, x-rays and gamma-rays alike. Thus the great bulk of the sun, pouring out radiation in light and heat will continually diminish in mass. There is no reason to doubt that in all processes of power production which we use in industrial and domestic life mass is actually lost. However, the amount of mass which would have to be annihilated in order to produce a large quantity of energy, as judged by our human standards, is extremely small. The work required, for instance, to lift a car on to the roof of a house is equivalent to a loss of mass of only 1/20,000,000,000,000 ounces. Because this loss of mass connected with our known means of production of power is so very minute, it passes unnoticed in everyday affairs; but in the sun where the production of power takes place on an enormous scale, the annihilation of mass accompanying the release of energy is significant. The sun looses no less than 4,200,000 tons of its mass in the form of radiation every second. Yet in spite of this the sun is so huge that its calculated life is at least 15,000 million years, which is as long a time as earthly requirements can reasonably demand..

Not only is the release of atomic energy the sole agent

known to us which is capable of explaining the radiation of the stars, but also there exists direct evidence that atom splitting and atom building is going on in the universe at large. Coming in showers like rain all over the surface of the earth, rays burst upon us with enormous energy from every quarter of the sky. These are the so-called "cosmic rays," which have already been encountered in connection with positive electrons and mesons. Cosmic rays do not affect our lives as far as we can tell, for mercifully they are thinly spread, but their energy is so great that they could have been generated only by nuclear changes somewhere far off in the universe. Where and how cosmic rays are generated is not known, but their occurrence provides striking evidence that atomic transmutations can and do proceed spontaneously under conditions obtaining in the depths of space.

To return to the question of the sun, what exactly are the nuclear changes taking place inside it which supply its energy? Some time ago astronomers suggested that these transmutations may be the same or nearly the same as the natural radioactive changes occuring on the earth. Of late, however, it has became doubtful if heavy elements such as are responsible for radioactive decay on earth can exist in the centre of the sun, which like all stars is composed most abundantly of hydrogen. Today it is generally accepted that the fuel of the sun must be its own hydrogen, which by continually being transformed into helium is capable of producing energy in the required amount.

In the interior of the sun the temperature is about 20 million degrees centigrade, more than 3000 times hotter than the surface we can see. The pressure, too, is very great, being nearly 900 million times greater than the pressure of the atmosphere on the surface of the earth. Under these extreme conditions hydrogen nuclei exist as protons, having no electronic cloud around them as they have when encountered here on earth. They collide with each other with such frequency that atomic transformations happen all the time. Such high temperatures as these in the centre of the sun are difficult to comprehend, but their essential feature is reflected in the high speed with which the protons move about.

Just before the war a theory suggesting the type of

nuclear transmutations going on in the sun's core was put forward by Bethe of Cornell University. By considering the various kinds of atomic reactions which had been observed in the laboratory, he concluded that in most stars helium nuclei are being built up by combination of four protons. Heavier elements than helium are not formed, since they would be broken down at once to helium again by the action of further bombardment by protons. The simplest way of building up a helium nucleus from hydrogen would be by a direct coalescence of four protons, two of which would have to change in the process into neutrons by giving birth to a positive electron. Bethe was able to show conclusively that such a process, occuring in a number of stages, will actually take place in stars, particularly in the colder ones, but that it will be somewhat too slow to account for the total energy produced by the sun. He proposed another, more complicated chain of reactions as the most likely process of provid-

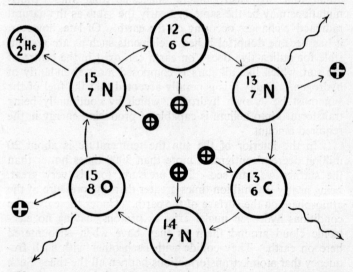

Fig. 26. *This is the cyclic process by means of which the sun changes Hydrogen into Helium. Four protons, shown inside the cycle, are transformed into an alpha-particle and two positive electrons. Gamma-rays are emitted at three stages and they as well as the speed of the newly formed particles provide the energy for the sun's radiation.*

ing energy release in the sun and this scheme has now been generally accepted. It postulates that instead of joining up directly with each other, protons will stand a better chance of forming alpha-particles by bombarding carbon nuclei. When an ordinary carbon atom, $^{12}_{6}C$, is hit by a proton it will be transformed into the nitrogen istope, $^{13}_{7}N$, which is unstable and which by ejecting a positive electron turns itself into the carbon istotope $^{13}_{6}C$. When this product is transmuted by bombardment with a further proton it changes into a nordinary nitrogen nucleus, $^{14}_{7}N$. This in turn is hit by another proton and made into the unstable oxygen isotope, $^{15}_{8}O$, which by emitting a positive electron forms another nitrogen isotope, $^{15}_{7}N$. When this is finally hit by yet another proton it breaks up into the carbon nucleus $^{12}_{6}C$ and a helium nucleus $^{4}_{2}He$. Thus at the end of the chain the original carbon atom reappears having passed through six different transmutations in the course of which four protons have disappeared and one alpha-particle plus two positive electrons have been created. In three of the stages gamma-rays are also emitted which we have, for simplicity's sake, left out of the account. It is clear that the carbon nucleus which reappears at the end of the chain can now again be employed in the formation of a new alpha-particle. In fact the whole process can best be represented as a continuous cycle in which carbon atoms are instrumental in turning hydrogen into helium without themselves being changed permanently. In ordinary chemistry this ability of certain substances to stimulate a reaction without being consumed in it is well known and ample use is made of these " catalysts " in industrial processes.

By making the reasonable assumption that carbon atoms account for one or two per cent of the mass of the stars, Bethe has calculated the rate of power production which his catalytic process would yield. When his calculations were compared with the measurements of the radiation from a number of stars, they were found to be in excellent agreement. There is thus every reason to believe that Bethe's ingenious chain of nuclear processes, discovered in the laboratory and computed on paper, represents the solution of the problem of stellar energy.

Although the most sensitive instruments are incapable of detecting the minute loss in weight which accompanies the chemical production of energy, as for example in the burning of coal or in the explosion of T.N.T. the change in mass which goes with the release of atomic energy can be measured. Up to now it has been assumed that, because all nuclei are built up of protons and neutrons, each with the weight of 1 unit, the weight of every atom must be a whole number. Thus hydrogen was assumed to have the weight 1, helium 4 and oxygen 16. While this is almost true it is not quite exact. Small deviations from this rule occur and are of the greatest significance in the question of atomic energy. Careful measurements have shown that the oxygen atom does not weigh exactly 16 times as much as the proton, but only 15.86 times. Since for purely practical reasons the standard for atomic weighing has not been based on hydrogen with weight 1 but on oxygen with weight 16, the accurate weight of the proton is taken to be 1.008. Using the same scale, the weight of the alpha-particle, as determined by experiment, is 4.003. The total weight of four protons (4.032) which are consumed in the energy production of the sun is therefore a little greater than the weight of the resulting helium nucleus. The differ-

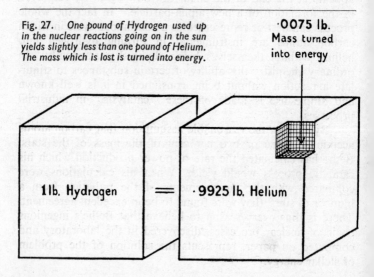

Fig. 27. *One pound of Hydrogen used up in the nuclear reactions going on in the sun yields slightly less than one pound of Helium. The mass which is lost is turned into energy.*

·0075 lb.
Mass turned
into energy

1 lb. Hydrogen = ·9925 lb. Helium

ence is roughly .03 units of weight and this is the mass which is turned into energy. Because of the very large energy liberated in nuclear reactions, the loss in weight, or " mass defect " as it is called, can be measured and it provides a most useful indication of the power which can be obtained from a given transmutation. Whereas the chemist who studies the formation or the breaking up of a compound must actually carry out the reaction and measure the amount of heat set free, the nuclear physicist can predict how much energy will be liberated when one atom is changed into another simply by weighing the atoms concerned. Not only will the difference in the weights tell him how much energy is going to be produced, but it also will indicate in which direction the reaction will proceed. The only changes that can take place spontaneously are those in which energy is liberated. The greater weight of the four protons therefore shows that without a supply of energy from outside they could never be formed by the spontaneous break up of an alpha-particle. Thus the mass defect between the nuclei bears evidence that in the sun hydrogen is changed into helium and not vice versa.

Besides the formation of helium from protons which is responsible for the radiation of the sun and of stars similar to it, a number of other nuclear changes are thought to provide the necessary energy in stars of different type. Scientists generally believe that with only a few exceptions all stars throughout the universe pass through the same successive stages of development just as the individual passes from childhod to adolescence, from adolescence to manhood and finally to old age. It is thought that the different aspect which the various stars present is not so much due to their being different in kind as different in age. The whole subject of stellar evolution, of necessity is one in which conjecture and speculation plays a very great part but a realisation of the atomic processes involved in stellar life has elucidated many problems. Modern theory presumes that stars are formed by the slow contraction of large masses of matter which are pulled together through gravitational attraction. The motion of particles towards a common centre, like the dropping of a stone, produces a release of

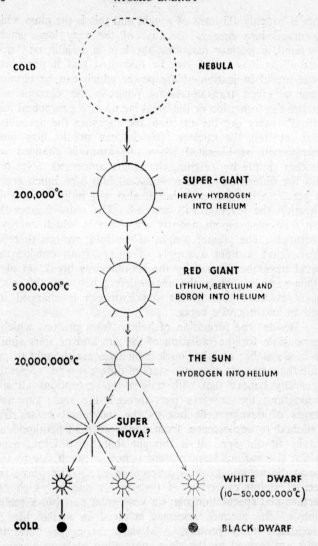

Fig. 28. *The theory of stellar evolution. The arrows indicate stages of contraction. It is impossible to draw the relative sizes of stars to scale since the contraction of a super-giant to a black dwarf would correspond to the shrinking of a full sized balloon to a grain of sand.*

energy and heat is involved. When the temperature reaches about 200,000 degrees centigrade, the first nuclear reactions begin to happen and these supply additional energy. At first atoms of heavy hydrogen, consisting of 1 proton and 1 neutron each, combine to form helium. When the supply of heavy hydrogen is exhausted in this way the star continues to collapse for about 10,000 years or so and reaches a temperature of about 5,000,000 degrees. Then the light elements that are present, lithium, beryllium, and boron for example, begin to react with protons in much the same way as was observed by Cockcroft and Walton in their disintegration experiments (page 46) and also form helium. As soon as these light elements are used up a further contraction takes place and the temperature in the core of the star rises to 20 million degrees. This is the state in which the sun is at present and which is estimated to last for about 10,000 million years. This is the longest period in the life of a star in which it feeds on its own hydrogen, changing it to helium. At last, when almost all hydrogen is consumed, the star again collapses but regarding what will happen in the end opinions are much divided. Some think that the shrinking process will go on undisturbed, while others hold that the star will break up. On the whole it is believed that in one way or another a "white dwarf" star will be formed as the final stage of extreme old age. Long before this stage is reached a development will have come to pass which is likely to terminate all life on earth. Gamow has shown that in its present hydrogen consuming stage the sun will, far from gradually cooling down become hotter and brighter all the time. Shortly before its hydrogen supply is exhausted, it will radiate a hundred times more light and heat than it does now. By then, the oceans and lakes on the surface of the earth will have boiled away and the last evidence of life will have vanished long before. In times less disturbing than the present one this forecast might have caused sombre reflection. Owing to its experience, our own generation will hardly be worried by the fate of mankind in 2,000 or 5,000 million years from now.

Whether this assessment of the development of the sun is correct in all details or not, one thing seems to be certain.

In none of the various periods of the generation of energy are heavy nuclei produced. On the contrary, even such light elements as lithium with an atomic weight of only 7 are broken up to form helium. In all stages of stellar life there seems to be no stage at which the elements found in such abundance in the crust of the earth could have been formed. It thus appears that the nuclei of uranium and thorium, which we can see breaking up continually, must have been carried over from another phase of the universe existing before the stars were born. At such a time matter must have existed at temperatures of some thousand million degrees, more than 50 times hotter than the hottest stars.

One of the oddest facts which astronomers have discovered in the last few decades is that on the average the stars throughout the universe seem to be moving away from us, and that the further they are away the more rapidly they recede. It is as if we stood on a fragment produced by an explosion of unbelievable and cosmic size. Those bits of the debris which were thrown out with the greatest speed have moved furthest away into the depths of space, while other, slower ones, have traversed only a shorter way; but all continue to move away from each other. By painstaking observations and calculations the beginning of the explosion has been determined. It seems to have happened about 2,000 million years ago. This, as we have seen, is also the age of the oldest rocks on the earth.

While it must be admitted that all these speculations contain a large element of uncertainty, the available evidence seems to point to a cosmological upheaval 2,000 million years ago in which the universe as we see it and also our earth were created. When the earth was born there must have existed in the universe a high degree of condensation of matter, probably coupled with enormous temperatures, in which the atoms which form the land, the sea and even our bodies were created. The energy which is released in the atomic bomb, too, was stored in the uranium nuclei in this bygone phase of the universe.

The great multitude of stars conforms to the pattern of orderly stellar development which is prescribed by theory; but there are exceptions. The satisfactory feature of the changes going on within the sun is that they proceed smoothly and steadily throughout the years, keeping the earth continually at the temperature required for life. By no means all stars do this. Some flicker up and down like a candle in the draught; some pulsate, expanding and contracting as they do so. Even these peculiar phenomena can probably be comprehended to some extent in the general scheme of stellar evolution. The flickering and oscillating stars are most probably those which are undergoing a change of life by turning from a steady state into one of contraction or vice versa. When this happens it may take some time until a proper balance of the different processes of energy production, collapse and nuclear reaction is restored, with the result that the star's radiation fluctuates for a while before it settles down.

There exists, however, a much more alarming variety of stars which are called "novae" or new stars. These stars which suddenly flare up in the sky are not newly created ones, but are new in the sense of being suddenly observable. They are stellar explosions in which the brightness of an ordinary star increases in the course of a few days by over 100,000 times. On June 7th 1918 the Nova Aquilae doubled its brightness in under an hour, blasting out at the same time a cloud of hot gases. This cloud which was thrown out with a speed of more than 4 million miles an hour had after six months increased to such a size that it could be seen with a telescope, appearing as a faint nebula enveloping the star. Quite a number of such nebulae are now known and it is fairly safe to assume that they are all the remains of stellar explosions (plate XII). In some cases a whole star is blown to bits when such a cataclysmic explosion takes place. The Nova Herculis which flared up on the 12th December 1934 was subsequently observed to have disintegrated into two separate stars flying apart with great speed.

As if this were not enough, there take place on rare occasions stellar catastrophies which outshine the ordinary novae by at least 10,000 times. Such a "super-nova" when bursting into light becames as brilliant as about a hundred million suns put together (plate XII). No such outburst has occurred in our galaxy for nearly four centuries. On the night of November 11th 1572 the great Danish astronomer Tycho Brahe when crossing the courtyard of his laboratory at Heridsvad observed a brilliant star which had suddenly appeared in the constellation of Cassiopeia. During the next few days this star became so bright that it could be seen in broad daylight. Its luminosity began to decrease in December and by the end of the year it had fallen to that of the planet Jupiter. In the following 16 months the star waned, changing its colour from white to yellow and then to red, and then disappeared completely. Another super-nova, in the constellation Taurus, was recorded by the Chinese in 1054 A.D. and it is possible that the star of Bethlehem, too, was such a super-nova. While there is no conclusive evidence for the existence of any remains of Tycho's star, an expanding shell of gas has been found in Taurus. From its rate of expansion it appears that it must have originated about 900 years ago.

The causes of these stellar explosions are quite unknown. There are reasons to doubt that their origin is due to a collision of stars with each other or with gas clouds. It appears that somehow a great store of atomic energy is "triggered off," as in the explosion of an atomic bomb; but no satisfactory theory as to the nature of the nuclear change involved has as yet been put forward. In recent years super-novae have been observed in distant galaxies and such material as has been gathered indicates that the total amount of energy liberated is not much greater than that radiated by a normal star when it converts its hydrogen in helium. However, instead of being spread out over many thousand million years, this energy is squandered in a few months.

When a star turns suddenly into a nova or a super-nova anything near at hand will be seared up in a wave of hot gas and radiation. It is therefore natural to speculate on the possibility of our sun bursting out in such a cataclysm; and one may ask what type of star is predisposed to become a nova and whether there are any previous indications that a star will do it. Since it is unknown which of the several ten thousand million stars in our galaxy will explode next, novae only become objects of attention after they have appeared and little is usually known about their previous state.

However, as good fortune will have it, the Nova Herculis had been investigated before it burst into light, and regrettably, the result of this investigation is not reassuring. Before catastrophe overtook it, the Nova Herculis was a star very much like our sun. Novae are however sufficiently rare occurrences to figure low among the obstacles to human survival. According to the laws of probability we are more likely to perish by famine, pestilence or by a man-made atomic bomb than by the action of a celestial one.

Bound up with the problem of the sun becoming a nova is the question whether the nova stage is one of natural development through which each star will pass or whether it is only an occasional aberration. Unless one assumes that their frequency changes with the age of the universe, supernovae occur far too seldom to allow every star to indulge in such a fling within its estimated lifetime. On the other hand, about ten stars become ordinary novae every year in our galaxy and this is a sufficiently high number to allot one or more explosions to the life of an average star. In view of these figures one begins to suspect that there are short lived but important phases in ordinary stellar evolution which are not covered by the existing theories.

Leaving these details aside, we can summarise stellar development as the contraction of a gas cloud under the force of gravity which is retarded by the liberation of atomic energy. The more a star contracts, the hotter will it become and the increase in temperature brings into play the series of nuclear reactions outlined above. In the end all the atomic energy is exhausted and the star is turned almost completely into helium. However, it does not vanish, only something like one percent of its total mass having been changed into radiation. One might conclude therefore that the star will now cool off and become a large sphere of solid helium. This however is not possible. Atoms as we know them on earth are very loosely built structures, consisting in the main of empty space, and they can only exist in this state if no undue pressure is exerted upon them from outside. The Indian physicist Kothari has calculated that if a pressure of 10 million atmospheres or more is brought to bear on atoms, their extravagant electronic clouds will be squashed out of existence. Owing to the sun's enormous weight the pressure in its interior far exceeds this value and when its atomic energy has been spent, it will collapse into what Gamow has aptly called the " crushed state of matter." It is impossible to make a heap of ping pong balls as high as Mount Everest because they would be crushed under their own weight. It is similarly impossible for a large cold astronomical body to be built up of ordinary atoms. The greater the mass of a body, the more will its matter be crushed and to a smaller size will it ultimately collapse. Kothari has estimated that the planets Jupiter and Saturn are about the largest cold bodies which can exist, and even their interior is already crushed or, as the physicist says, degenerate. The sun for all its present size will, in the end, be not much larger than the earth.

In this state of extreme degeneracy, in which nuclei and electrons are tightly compressed in a concentrated mash, the enormous mass of the sun will be accommodated in a sphere of not more than 10,000 miles diameter. A piece of matter from the dead sun of the size of a walnut would weigh many tons. Stars of such extreme densities as these have indeed been discovered. They are called white dwarfs. This process of further gravitational contraction, below the size of ordinary matter, furnishes another instalment of energy which will allow the star to go on radiating for a hundred million more years before it turns into a " black dwarf," a cold degenerate piece of matter. It is, of course, unknown whether this final stage exists in our universe since a black dwarf is unobservable. If there are such dead suns, they must be small globes of enormous weight consisting of crushed atoms and covered with a thin layer of liquid helium.

Since only one percent of the mass of a star is changed into radiation, one may ask whether there is not perhaps another store of atomic energy locked up within stars which may give them still another lease of life. It has indeed been suggested that in the final collapse of stars somewhat bigger than the sun, the atomic nuclei will be compressed to such an extent that they fuze into each other, creating a still more condensed state of matter. Concerning the properties of such a state one has only the vaguest ideas, but it is possible that its appearance may be accompanied by a further release of energy. Attempts have been made to explain the occurrence of super-novæ on this basis, and some physicists believe that the white dwarfs existing at present are the relics of stellar explosions, since the estimated age of the universe is too short already to have produced white dwarfs merely by the contraction of the stars.

Cosmological speculations have thus conjured up a multitude of processes for the generation of energy as well as a number of strange modifications of matter with which the universe is populated. They all serve to underline the exceptional character of terrestrial conditions. It is amusing to reflect that for centuries past scientists have been ponderously laying down the laws of physics on the most odd and unrepresentative morsel of matter which could possibly be chosen in the whole of the universe.

CHAPTER EIGHT

NUCLEAR FISSION

HIGH above the beautiful old city of Prague towers the Hradcin, the ancient castle of the kings of Bohemia. Within its precincts, crowded with palaces and churches, there stands a huddled row of tiny houses which in spite of its shabbiness bears the grand name Zlata Ulice or Golden Lane. This was once a secret government research station, where more than 300 years ago the emperor Rudolph II kept his alchemists. The object of their work was, of course, to replenish the treasury with artificially produced gold, and it is thus not surprising that the imperial government did not like to take chances and confined the alchemists to the immediate neighbourhood of its offices. In our more enlightened times, we are inclined to pass harsh judgment on alchemists, and tend to look upon them as ignorant charlatans or cunning swindlers. However, while it was the stated purpose of these gentlemen to discover the manufacture of gold, it appears that many of them became so engrossed in the marvellous and intriguing transformations that happened in their crucibles and alembics that they strayed far from their immediate task. One can well imagine that it was only when the annual application form for the renewal of their research grant came round that they remembered their calling and quickly scribbled under the heading "Purpose of research" the words: "Discovery of philosopher's stone." As to the emperor, he seems to have aided and abetted in their fundamental research to a large extent, becoming himself an amateur scientist and astronomer and preferring learned speculation and his vast collections to the somewhat involved international relations of his day.

Neither emperor nor alchemists can really be blamed for their lapses. Before their eyes there began to be unfolded the mysterious and colourful world of chemical changes. Marble was turned into gas and metal into salt. To men who could do this, nothing seemed impossible. As yet there was no system and boundary to the abundance of newly created substances and to the reactions by which one was changed into another. Progress was exciting but, to say the least, bewildering.

In the past twenty-five years, nuclear physicists have been in much the same position as were the alchemists centuries ago. After Rutherford had succeeded in changing the atoms of nitrogen into those of oxygen, an ever growing host of scientists tried their hand at finding new and surprising types of nuclear changes. In the preceding chapters of this book we have mentioned a number of nuclear reactions which in their haphazard occurrence may have been as bewildering to the reader as they were to the physicists who discovered them. We have encountered all sorts of particles and nuclei which were shot into one another either in the laboratory or in the centre of the sun, and from these reactions there have issued forth more nuclei and particles as well as electro-magnetic waves. The reader may be consoled by the fact that even the most expert nuclear physicists find it difficult to pick their way through this great mass of mostly unconnected results. Only gradually do the main trends and laws of nuclear changes begin to stand out from the vast amount of material collected. It is a blessing in disguise that technical development has restricted research up to now to experiments with only the lightest particles as projectiles and mainly light nuclei as targets. In this way the number of observable reactions has been somewhat limited and can be subjected more easily to a systematic survey. In the diagram on page 120 the most important types of nuclear reactions known at present are listed. They are restricted to four kinds of bombarding particles; protons, alpha-particles, nuclei of heavy hydrogen (usually called deuterons) and neutrons. It should be mentioned that nuclear changes can also be produced by subjecting nuclei to gamma-rays, but these reactions occur more rarely.

When a particle is shot into a nucleus, a new nucleus is formed. This " compound nucleus " houses, besides the particles contained in the original nucleus, the newly added one. The bombarding particle, apart from adding itself to

PROTON BOMBARDMENT:

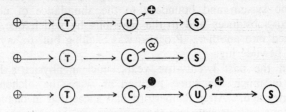

DEUTERON BOMBARDMENT

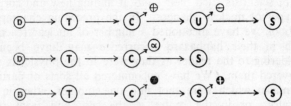

ALPHA-PARTICLE BOMBARDMENT:

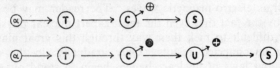

NEUTRON BOMBARDMENT:

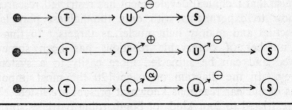

Fig. 29. *A list of the most important types of nuclear reaction. The target nucleus (T), when hit by a particle, usually turns into a compound nucleus (C) which after emission of another particle becomes an unstable nucleus (U). From this a stable nucleus (S) is formed after emission of a negative or positive electron. Sometimes the bombarding particle is captured and no particle is emitted except an electron. Gamma-radiation which may occur at different stages is not shown in the diagram.*

the other nuclear particles, contributes its energy of motion which it now shares with the rest of the nucleus. Bohr, to whom this description of nuclear reactions is due, has compared the process of bombardment to the projection of a marble into a trough. If the trough contains only a few marbles, that is, if it is a very light nucleus containing only a few particles, the entering marble stands a chance of passing right through without encountering any obstacle inside the trough. It will leave the trough on the other side, and no reaction will take place. On the other hand, in a trough containing a fair number of marbles, the bombarding marble is bound to collide with them and make them all move. The result is that instead of one marble having a high velocity, all of them will have lower velocities and yet none of them will be fast enough to spill over the side of the trough. A compound nucleus is formed (plate VII).

If we would try to imitate an atomic collision in this way with a dish and some marbles we would find that in due course the movement of all the marbles dies down owing to friction. However, there is no friction inside a nucleus and on the atomic scale the movement will persist until by an extremely rare chance all the energy is again concentrated in the motion of one particle which then will escape. This probability of escape from a compound nucleus which has an unduly high energy is, of course, the same process which we have described in slightly different terms in chapter 5. There it was stated that in a radioactive atom an alpha-particle " leaks through " the walls of the trough because its de Broglie wave penetrates them. This wave, as we have seen, denotes the probability of finding the particle outside the nucleus. The nuclei of uranium can thus be regarded as compound nuclei which were formed when the universe was young and which are unstable. The chance of an alpha-particle escaping from an uranium nucleus is so rare that to this day it has not happened in many of them. This is a very different situation from most artificial transmutations in which the compound nucleus has a much shorter life time and where bombardment is followed almost immediately by ejection of a particle.

Bohr has pointed out that the mechanical model of a

trough filled with marbles, while useful for visualising the
state of a compound nucleus, cannot fully describe what is
in fact a quantum-mechanical problem. The pretty analogy
will, however, serve to convey the main features of the results
of nuclear bombardment. A compound nucleus is one which
has received together with a new particle an excess amount
of energy and which therefore is unstable. In order to
become stable, it must get rid of its surplus energy in one
way or another. The list of nuclear reactions on page 120
shows what these ways are. The compound nucleus may
pack off the unwanted energy simply by sending it forth in
the form of a gamma-ray, or it may eject a particle, or it may
turn one of its protons into a neutron (or vice versa) and
thereby give birth to a positive or negative electron. It is an
interesting feature of nuclear changes that one and the same
compound nucleus may undergo any of these transmutations
or that several transmutations may happen successively.
Whether one or the other change takes place is merely a
question of probability. Like business men in free trade the
different processes of energy removal stand in open competi-
tion and the one which offers the speediest service to the
overburdened nucleus will carry off the biggest yield. For
instance, the transmutation of a proton into a neutron with
the subsequent manufacture of an electron is a slow and
cumbersome process standing little chance compared with
the fast business of emission of a gamma-ray or a neutron.
Only when these more efficient competitors have left so little
excess energy that there is insufficient to eject another particle,
is there scope for electron emission. If, for example, boron,
B, is bombarded with protons it is most likely that the
compound nucleus, $^{12}_{6}C$, formed by capture of a proton will
get rid of its surplus energy by disgorging almost instantaneously a neutron. The resulting nucleus, $^{11}_{6}C$, will live
for about 20 minutes and then by emitting a positive electron
turn back into $^{11}_{5}B$. As the list (page 120) shows this return
to stability by stages, of which the electron emission is the
last, is a common process.

In one very important respect the trough and marble
model is quite inadequate. Like electrons in an atom's
external cloud, nuclear particles can occupy only certain

definite energy levels, and if one is shot into the neucleus with an energy corresponding to one of these levels, its chance of entering and remaining in the nucleus is much enhanced. One observes therefore, that, contrary to the classical model, bombarding particles with certain definite velocities are particularly effective. Here again the bombarding particle behaves rather like a wave. A radio receiver, tuned to a certain wavelength, will take up just this particular wavelength, and a tuning fork will respond only to one particular note. This phenomenon is known as resonance, and the preferential capture of nuclear particles with definite velocities is therefore called "resonance capture."

In the list of nuclear reactions there appears a type of change which has not yet been discussed. This is the reaction produced by bombardment with neutrons. All the early transmutation experiments were carried out by shooting positively charged particles, protons and helium nuclei, into the target atoms. When discussing Cockcroft and Walton's experiment on the bombardment of lithium by protons, we mentioned that the chance of scoring a hit is only about one in a million. The reason for this low efficiency is twofold. First a nucleus is such a small target that a bombarding particle will have to travel through about 100 million atoms before it hits a nucleus. In its passage through the electron clouds the positively charged bombarding particle attracts to it negative electrons all the time and in doing so loses its energy. It is this process which produces the visible tracks. The intruder stands in fact a 1000 to 1 chance of losing virtually all its speed in this way before it even encounters a nucleus in its path. Secondly those few fortunate ones which meet a nucleus are by no means certain of successful entry. They are faced, as it were, with the steep outer slope of a volcano, and unless they are aimed dead true and have sufficient speed, they will roll off the side of the slope and fail to enter the nucleus. In other words the particle is repelled and deflected by the like positive charge of the nucleus, and the likelihood of its being deflected increases rapidly when the heavier nuclei, which bear strong positive charges, are attacked (plate V).

A comet approaching the vicinity of the solar system

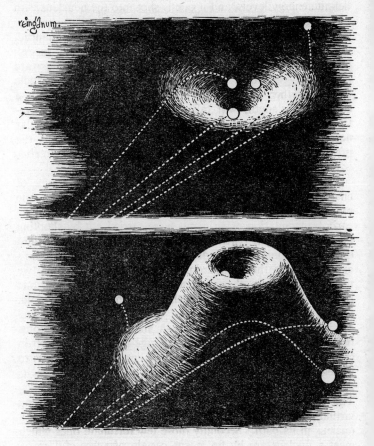

reingnum.

Fig. 30.   *The appearance presented by the nuclear energy trough to: (above) a
neutron; and (below) a positively charged particle.*

will on the other hand suffer a very different fate. Round
the energy trough of the sun, there is no barrier preventing
the comet's entry. On the contrary it will be swallowed up
as soon as it reaches the inclined slope and will remain the
sun's captive like the earth and the planets. Only if the
comet had initially a high speed, would it stand a chance of

escaping again before settling down in an orbit around the sun, somewhat like the ball in a game of Bar Billiards.

The steep external slope of the nuclear trough is, as we have seen, produced by its positive charge. For a neutral particle, on the other hand, this barrier does not exist. To a neutron making its way towards a nucleus, the latter appears just as the solar trough does to a comet or like a hole in the ground to a marble. Every neutron heading for a nucleus, unless it bounches out of the trough, will be captured by it. Moreover, because it has no charge a neutron will not interfere with the electronic clouds through which it passes. Thus the two obstacles which reduce the rate of transmutation by charged particles, the electronic cloud and the positive charge of the nucleus, do not exist for neutrons, and it is clear that they must therefore be very efficient sub-atomic bullets. Thus the discovery of the neutron not only was of paramount importance for the theory of nuclear constitution, but also it provided physicists with a new and excellent weapon with which to attack even the heaviest nuclei.

Because of the quantum nature of the nuclear trough, the ability of a neutron to cause transmutation again depends on its speed. If its energy of motion happens to correspond with one of the energy levels of the nucleus attacked, the neutron will remain in the nucleus and thereby produce a change. However, if the neutron's velocity is not " in resonance " with one of these levels, it will bounce out again. Whereas the heavier nuclei have so many energy levels that they can accommodate neutrons of practically any speed, the lighter ones are not so fortunate. In particular from the nuclei of ordinary and heavy hydrogen, of helium and of carbon, neutrons of almost all speeds will bounce off. A neutron which is shot into any of these substances will, like a billiard ball shot into the pyramid, share its energy of motion with the nuclei with which it collides and thus be slowed down. This slowing down of neutrons by collisions with light nuclei as well as their capture by resonance are processes of the utmost importance in the release of atomic energy.

Owing to the facility with which they can be captured, there are not many unattached neutrons at large in the world in spite of the fact that neutrons account for more than half of the earth's weight. In order to obtain free neutrons, atomic nuclei must be bombarded with charged particles. It would thus seem that the discovery of the neutron had merely shifted the bottleneck limiting the production of artificial transmutation and the release of atomic energy to another stage. However, neutron bullets permit reactions involving the heaviest nuclei, and it was in the study of these reactions that the key to the release of atomic energy was found.

The series of chemical elements breaks off with uranium, number 92, and for a long time scientists have been tantalized by the question of what was beyond this limit. After it had been established that uranium in a series of radioactive transmutations gives birth to lead, the problem arose as to what element gave birth to uranium. No such parent element could be found either on the earth or by analysis of the light which comes to us from the sun and the stars. It became clear that elements heavier than uranium, if they ever existed, must have vanished completely from the observable universe, and got lost for ever. However, like the alchemists at the time of the Renaissance, the scientists of the twentieth century feel that there is no thing which man cannot accomplish. It must have been with thoughts such as these in mind that in 1934 the Italian physicist Fermi set out to recreate "transuranic" elements, which had died out a thousand million years ago.

Fermi's experiment consisted of the bombardment of nuclei of uranium and other heavy elements by neutrons. As the list of nuclear reations on page 120 shows, a neutron is likely to be captured, and the resulting unstable nucleus will then probably emit a negative electron. The bombardment of uranium $^{238}_{92}$ U, by neutrons should therefore produce first by neutron capture $^{239}_{92}$U and then by electron emission the nucleus $^{239}_{93}$?, because a neutron is turned into a proton. This hypothetical element has the atomic number 93 and thus would stand *above* uranium in the list of chemical elements.

The trouble with Fermi's experiment was that it was too successful. The bombardment resulted indeed in the production of radioactive nuclei, but instead of one or two types, a great number of different nuclei made their appearance. Some of these seemed to belong to the expected transuranic elements but for the others identification was almost impossible. Experiments similar to those of Fermi and his co-workers were soon carried out in a number of laboratories, particularly in Paris and Berlin. However, instead of becoming clearer the situation grew even more confused. More and more nuclei were discvoered and it became increasingly difficult to fit them into any reasonable scheme. Identification of new and so far unknown chemical elements is a difficult matter, particularly when the total number of atoms available is comparatively small and when the nuclei continually change their identity in radioactive transmutations.

By 1938 the situation regarding the transuranic elements had become quite hopeless. The Paris research workers found a nucleus which behaved like the element lanthanum and for this it was harder to find a place above uranium than for any of the others. Then something happened which showed that the whole conception underlying the experiments was untenable. Hahn and Strassmann in Berlin repeated the Paris experiment and found that one of the nuclei produced seemed to be radium which has the atomic number 88. This appeared to be quite unbelievable since in changing from number 92 to 88, the uranium nucleus would have to disgorge two alpha-particles in succession, and no alpha-particles were observed in the experiment. In order to prove that the nuclei observed really were radium, Hahn and Strassmann set about isolating them chemically. This is done first by separating radium together with barium from all the other elements and then by separating radium from barium. All went well up to the radium-barium separation, and then came the great surprise; the new radioactive nuclei were not radium but barium!

The full significance of the discovery was realised at once. As a barium atom has only a little more than half the weight of the uranium atom, it was clear that the uranium atom must have been shattered to bits. Subsequent experiments showed that the uranium nucleus when subjected to neutron bombardment indeed broke up into two fragments of almost equal size. This new process of " nuclear fission," as it has been called, is vastly different from any other known reaction. Up till this time the largest piece ever broken off a nucleus was an alpha-particle, and with this in mind it is not surprising that it took so long for scientists to realise that in Fermi's experiment a quite different and unexpected process was initiated.

When the Berlin physicists reported their observations on barium obtained from uranium in the first days of 1939, Frisch and Miss Meitner, two scientists who had left Nazi Germany, immediately realised the true nature of this new type of nuclear reaction, suggesting an explanation of its mechanism. They pointed out that the breaking up of heavy nuclei into two almost equal fragments fitted in well with Bohr's ideas concerning the structure of the atomic nucleus. These ideas had been developed along the lines of the so-called " liquid drop model " which has already been mentioned in chapter 6.

We often observe that small quantities of liquid dropped on to a flat surface, instead of spreading out like a lake or a puddle, form droplets. Indeed, the phenomenon is so exceedingly common that we never stop to think of why it happens. Nevertheless many of us will be at a loss when asked for an explanation. In a lump of ice the molecules are held rigidly in their places, and are bound tightly together by attraction forces. These forces are largely overcome when ice is melted and turned into water, but even in a liquid there remain slight forces of attraction between neighbouring molecules. Thus a small amount of water can be held together by these forces of cohesion which tend to make the surface as small as possible. The result is the formation of a spherical droplet. Atomic nuclei, too, are assemblies of particles which are kept together by the nuclear exchange forces and since one has reason to believe that, like molecules in a liquid, nuclear particles can move about freely, the whole nucleus to some extent resembles a miniature droplet.

Anyone who has played with the pretty drops of mercury spilt from a broken thermometer will have noticed that the smaller the droplets are, the more spherical is their shape. When a greater amount of mercury is gathered together, the pretty shape is lost and the drops become flatter and flatter

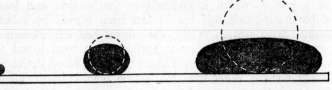

Fig. 31. *The bigger a drop, the less spherical is its shape.*

as they grow in size. In the end they become so flat that they are no longer drops. This maximum size of a drop is, of course, not a peculiarity of mercury but is shared by all liquids. Nobody has ever seen a drop of water as large as a football! The reason for this is that as the drop grows the gravitational force of the earth gradually outweighs the short range cohesive forces within the drop and pulls the drop out flat. The force which in atomic nuclei counteracts the mutual attraction of the particles is the electric repulsion between the protons, and this must become more and more noticeable as the nucleus grows in size. It is evidently for this reason that the heavier nuclei require such a substantial surplus of neutrons to keep them together. Finally, even the neutron surplus will be of no avail and, just as there is a natural limit to the size of water drops, there must be a similar limit to the size of nuclei. Rough calculations have shown that this limit will lie somewhere near the atomic number 100. This fits in well with the fact that nuclei with atomic numbers larger than 83 (bismuth) are radioactive, spontaneously breaking up since they are already too large.

When energy is put into a drop of water, it responds by ejecting single molecules, that is to say some of the water evaporates. Similarly, a nucleus when submitted to bombardment will get rid of a particle or a gamma-ray. However, as Frisch and Miss Meitner pointed out, there is a different way in which a large flatish drop of liquid can react to the application of energy. It can break up into two smaller and more spherical drops. This shattering of a large drop into smaller fragments, an every day observation, has its counterpart in the world of nuclei, in the process of fission.

It appears from these considerations that fission ought to

be a process which is confined to the heaviest and least stable nuclei, and this has in fact been proved by subsequent experiments. Only the three heaviest elements, uranium, protoactinium and thorium, have been found to undergo fission. One should also expect that blows delivered at the nucleus, other than by neutron bombardment, might have a similar effect, and this, too, has turned out to be the case. Heavy nuclei can be shattered by alpha-particles, deuterons, protons and even gamma-rays.

When the news of Hahn and Strassmann's discovery broke in January 1939, it resulted in a veritable explosion of scientific activity all over the world. Professor Bohr, who was at that time attending a scientific meeting in Washington, discussed the problem with his American colleagues, and the speed with which the matter was taken up is best shown by the fact that the issue of the *Physical Review* published on February 15th carried no less than four individual accounts of confirmatory experiments. Much the same sort of thing was happening in Europe, where Joliot in Paris reported similar results in the *Comptes Rendus* of January 30th, and Frisch in Copenhagen sent a letter to *Nature* which was published on February 18th also describing the observation of fission.

The great importance which physicists all over the world attached to the new discovery was not merely due to the fact that nuclear fission was so far an unknown type of reaction. Previous research on the properties of different nuclei indicated that this new kind of transmutation should be accompanied by an extraordinary release of energy. As early as 1919 Aston of Cambridge had developed an ingenious instrument, called the "mass spectrograph" (plate IX), which made it possible to determine the weight of the individual nuclei. This apparatus had revealed that most elements contain isotopes, that is nuclei of different weight, and in the years following much work had been done on the accurate determination of the weights of all existing nuclei. These experiments had uncovered the peculiar fact that the mass of a nucleus is not exactly the sum of the weights of the individual protons and neutrons of which the nucleus is made up. We have already encountered this phenomenon in the combination of four protons to form one helium atom which takes place in the sun. We have seen that the mass of four separate protons is greater than that of the resulting helium nucleus, and that this difference in mass, the " mass defect " is changed into energy.

By comparing the atomic weights determined with the mass spectrograph in passing from lighter to heavier nuclei it has been found that the difference between the weight of the nuclei and that of the separate building bricks from which they are made up, increases steadily. In other words, as heavier nuclei are built up by adding protons and neutrons, energy will be liberated. There are a few exceptions to this rule among the very lightest nuclei, but in general it can be said that energy can only be gained by building up nuclei and not by breaking them down. The mass defect is thus a measure of the energy with which the nuclear particles are bound together. However, as heavier nuclei are built up, the electric repulsion of the protons will make itself felt more and more, and will begin to outweigh the attraction due to the nuclear exchange forces. The balance appears to be reached at atomic weights of about 60, representing the elements nickel and iron, and from then upwards energy must be used up in adding further particles. In spite of this, the series of stable elements continues up to bismuth with an atomic weight of 209, and it is natural to wonder why these elements are not radioactive, decaying to nickel and iron. The answer is that in order to break up, these nuclei would obviously have to pass through a stage of higher energy, just as water from a pail cannot run out on the floor unless it is first lifted over the rim. When this extra energy is added, the heavier nuclei ought to break up, and it is significant that the core of the earth consists of iron and nickel and therefore seems to be at the very end of all spontaneous nuclear changes.

While no method is known by which this general disintegration of atoms higher on the list than nickel and iron can be achieved, fission provides such a means for the three heaviest nuclei. From the measured mass defects it is clear that, when a uranium nucleus breaks up in fission, the weight of the fragments will be smaller than that of the original

Fig. 32.   The fission fragments weigh less than the Uranium atom did before it broke up.   The lost mass is changed into energy.

nucleus and a very considerable amount of energy must be released.   Using different methods, Frisch and Joliot in fact showed that this energy appears when uranium nuclei are bombarded with neutrons.   The way in which uranium undergoes fission is evidently somewhat haphazard, individual atoms breaking up into different kinds of fragments.   The two resulting nuclei usually have weights of about 140 and 90 and may belong to a great number of different elements, ranging from selenium to lanthanum.   These fission products are not stable nuclei but are radioactive isotopes which gradually decay into stable form by emitting electrons.   This means that not all of the energy released will be turned into energy of motion of the two fragments, but that a part will be lost in subsequent radioactive decay.   By 1940 the energy of the fragments had been measured and it was found that one pound of uranium undergoing fission would release about 10 million kilowatt-hours.   This experimental result is in fair agreement with the energy release that had been calculated from the mass defect.

A pound of uranium can supply sufficient power for the Atlantic crossing of a fair sized liner.   Innumerable comparisons of this kind have been used in the last twenty-five years to illustrate the huge amount of energy which is locked in atomic nuclei.   However, in the case of uranium fission

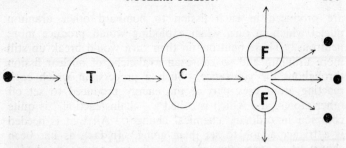

Fig. 33. *The fission process. When a heavy target nucleus (T) is hit by a neutron, an elongated compound nucleus (C) is formed which breaks up into two unstable fragments (F) and a number (between one and three) of neutrons. The fragments are positively charged but beyond the reach of the nuclear attraction forces and therefore fly apart with considerable energy.* (plate VII).

there is one feature which makes all the difference between utopia and reality. This feature is bound up with the proportion existing between protons and neutrons in different nuclei. As the nuclei become heavier an increasing proportion of neutrons is required to keep the protons together. Thus while the number of protons and neutrons in a light nucleus such as that of helium are equal (2 protons and 2 neutrons), the uranium nucleus contains 92 protons and as many as 146 neutrons. If this heavy nucleus breaks up into two lighter ones, there may appear therefore a number of surplus neutrons which are not needed in the construction of the lighter nuclei. Joliot and his co-workers Halban and Kowarski found in 1939 that the fission of uranium indeed produces such surplus neutrons, and their discovery was confirmed shortly afterwards by Anderson and others in America.

The emission of a number of neutrons from the fission process provides the key to the release of atomic energy. In the laboratory experiments conducted so far only now and again would a uranium nucleus which had been hit by a neutron explode. The energy produced in each case was immense on the atomic scale, but never more than one atom went off at a time. The total energy produced therefore was still very much smaller than that put in by neutron bombardment. However, matters would be very different, if it were possible to make use of the fresh supply of neutrons which are produced in each fission to bombard other uranium nuclei which in turn when exploding would produce more neutrons. These neutrons in their turn would break up still more uranium and so cause an avalanche of nuclear fission throughout the substance. Such a process, in which each reacting atom uses part of the energy produced to set off other atoms, and which is called a " chain reaction," is quite common in ordinary chemical changes. All that is needed is a trigger action to set them going. In fact, as has been shown in a previous chapter, all our power producing reactions like the burning of coal or the detonation of T.N.T. are of this type.

CHAPTER NINE

THE ATOMIC BOMB

BEFORE 1939 the release of atomic energy provided novelists from time to time with suitable material for sensational forecasts of the world to come in a hundred years, but any scientist would have considered the possibility as extremely remote. The general impression was that, whereas the interior of the sun with its very high temperature provided favourable conditions for nuclear reactions, no such processes were likely to happen on the surface of the earth. In order that such reactions might take place, nuclei must come into contact with each other or with other nuclear particles, and it appeared that the intervening electronic clouds would always constitute an unsurmountable barrier to the occurence of such meetings on a large scale. The discovery of fission in 1939, however, suddenly seemed to provide a means of liberating energy on a tremendous scale and the various possibilities were discussed among scientists and others in every country. Since man's mind works this way, the production of an atomic bomb figured largely among these possibilities. However, whether it could be made to work or not nobody could say. A short survey of the knowledge gained in the early experiments will make this clear.

The main outcome of the research on fission up to the end of 1939 can be summarised as follows. When uranium or other heavy nuclei are bombarded with neutrons they break up into two large fragments and this process is accompanied by a release of energy. The reaction will also produce a number of neutrons which should be capable of breaking up more nuclei.

It was therefore apparent that the fission process provides the necessary prerequisites for a self-propagating chain reaction. However, it was equally apparent that in the great number of laboratory experiments in which uranium had been bombarded not a single explosion had occured. Moreover, it was later found that on rare occasions a uranium nucleus may spontaneously undergo fission and thus liberate neutrons. On the other hand, in the last 150 years samples of uranium metal had been prepared for occasional laboratory experiments and have since been lying about peacefully in drawers and cupboards without blowing up. This shows clearly that the establishment of a nuclear chain reaction in uranium must require certain conditions which were not fulfilled in any of these cases.

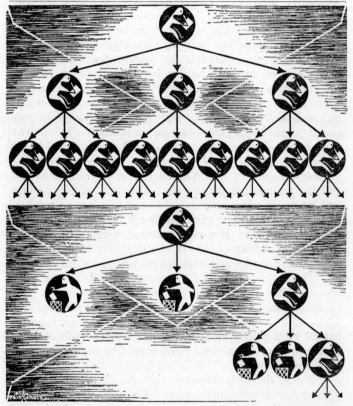

Fig. 34. *A self sustaining reaction can be compared with the writing of chain letters. The rate at which the reaction proceeds depends on the number of letters written at successive stages. If this increases rapidly (upper picture), the reaction will be of an explosive character.*

The conditions which have to be satisfied to maintain a self-sustaining reaction can be illustrated by the practice of writing " chain-letters." The recipient of such a chain-letter is usually asked to write a number of similar letters, say three, to his friends. If all recipients faithfully comply with this request the number of letter writers will steadily increase, and increase at an astonishing rate. While at the first stage only three letters are written, nine will be written at the second stage and twenty-seven at the third. At the tenth stage no less than 59,049 letters are being written and this figure will rise to 3,500 million letters at the twentieth stage.

On the other hand the matter will be very different if some of the recipients, instead of following instructions, throw the chain-letters which they have received into the waste paper basket and do nothing more about it. If two out of the three prospective letter writers choose to take this course, there will be only one letter written at each stage. Should at any stage all three recipients refuse to write, the chain will be broken and the whole process will die out. We thus see that the whole success of the scheme depends on the response which the letters are capable of provoking. It is clear that, in order to keep the process going, the number of letters in successive stages must increase or, at least, not diminish.

A nuclear chain reaction is a similar process in which the letters represent the neutrons and the recipients the uranium nuclei. No self-propagating reaction can take place unless the number of fissions in successive stages increase or, at least, maintains a constant level. The fact that no explosion has been observed to have taken place in any of the older experiments is therefore a clear indication that the neutrons emitted in the fission process must have failed to set off other nuclei. We have seen that in order to produce a chain, on the average at least one neutron from each individual fission must create another fission. Since it has been established that from each uranium nucleus which breaks up, more than one neutron is ejected, the inescapable conclusion is that some neutrons must have been lost from the process. Where had they gone?

The most obvious explanation is that neutrons leave the

metal and escape, never to return. In view of the fact that in any substance the atomic nuclei are few and far between, like apples placed at intervals of a few miles apart, a neutron will have to travel a considerable distance before it encounters a nucleus; and if the lump of uranium is small, the average neutron stands a good chance of escaping without hitting a nucleus. However, the bigger the lump of uranium, the smaller will be the chance of an average neutron escaping. For instance for spherical lumps, if the diameter is doubled, the chance of a neutron escaping is reduced to a quarter. This is so because the number of neutrons liberated is proportional to the volume of the metal, whereas the number escaping is proportional to the surface area, and as a sphere grows in size, its volume increases more rapidly than its surface area. On the basis of the available data, Perrin calculated that at least 40 tons of uranium oxide would have to be gathered into one lump before the escape of neutrons would be sufficiently reduced for a chain reaction to take place.

The number of neutrons available also depends very much on the purity of the material. We have seen that any nuclei, particularly the heavier ones, readily capture neutrons, and the presence of even a small numer of foreign atoms in the material may therefore seriously diminish the number of neutrons available for fission. Thus the establishment of a chain reaction requires the use of very pure uranium.

However, it soon became clear that even the largest size and the highest purity were not quantities themselves sufficient to ensure a chain reaction. If a lump of purest uranium metal as big as the Albert Hall could be manufactured it still would not explode, even when submitted to intense neutron bombardment. The reason for this is that not every neutron which scores a hit necessarily causes the bombarded uranium nucleus to break up in fission. When Fermi began his experiments in 1934, he proceeded under the assumption that the $^{238}_{92}U$ nuclei would capture the bombarding neutrons and form $^{239}_{92}U$. For a moment the discovery of fission overshadowed this problem of neutron capture; but the question came up again when the possibility of a chain reaction had to be considered. Experiments showed subsequently that the nucleus $^{238}_{92}$U (which for simplicity's sake we will call U.238) only breaks up in fission if it is hit by a neutron of high speed Neutrons with *moderate* speed, on the other hand are captured, and U.239 is formed *without* fission taking place. This capture of particles with a certain speed is the quantum-mechanical resonance phenomenon which we have encountered in the previous chapter, and it is due to the fact that the energy trough of U.238 contains an energy level exactly corresponding to a certain neutron speed. Thus while we can compare the escape of neutrons and their capture by impurities to chain letters which have been lost or which were delivered at the wrong address, the neutrons which disappear through resonance capture must be likened to the letters which have been thrown into the waste paper basket.

For a time it seemed as if the existence of resonance capture was destined to foil all schemes for releasing atomic energy. The experiments indeed showed that when the speed of the bombarding neutrons was lowered, fission diminished rapidly. However, there was one curious fact which did not fit at all into the general picture. It was that fission again became very noticeable when neutrons with the slowest speed were employed. The explanation of this curious phenomenon was furnished by a paper published by Bohr and Wheeler early in 1939. Their theory, which was based on Bohr's conception of nuclear reactions, ascribed the fission occuring with slow neutrons to the presence of a uranium isotope with weight 235.

There are three isotopes of uranium, U.238 which makes up 99.3% of the metal, U.235,* amounting to .7% and a very rare isotope U.234. The proportion of U.234 is so small (less than 1 in 10,000) that it can be neglected for all practical purposes; but U.235, although amounting to less than 1%, is most important for the fission process. Bohr and Wheeler pointed out that it is this isotope which is responsible for fission by slow neutrons and that it will not show resonance capture to any appreciable extent. In the following year a small batch of uranium metal containing a higher proportion of U.235 was prepared by Nier of Minnesota, and experiments on it fully confirmed the theoretical predictions.

---

* This is the radioactive parent of protactinium (see Appendix, 3).

The neutrons produced by the fission process originally have a high speed, but as they make their way through the substance they are slowed down by collisions. Only a few of these high speed neutrons cause fission of U.238 nuclei; the great majority, after being slowed down, are captured with the formation of U.239 and are lost from the fission process. A few which escape this fate eventually encounter a U.235 nucleus and break it up. A rough idea of what happens can be given in tabulated form:

Speed of neutron:	Reaction produced.
Fast	Fission of U.238 and to a lesser extent of U.235.
Medium	Resonance capture by U.238.
Slow	Fission of U.235.

Most of the fissions observed in experiments are due to the presence of the isotope U.235. It is unfortunate from the point of view of a chain reaction however, that only a few of the fast neutrons issuing from fission eventually hit and break up another U.235 nucleus. As we have just seen, most of them will be intercepted and swallowed up in resonance capture by U.238. It is this capture process more than anything else which reduces the number of neutrons available, and if a chain reaction is to be set going, this capture must be eliminated.

As soon as all this was realised, two schemes, one radical and the other elegant, were proposed by which it was hoped to eliminate resonance capture to such extent that a chain reaction would take place. The radical scheme is obvious and simply consists in separating the troublesome U.238 from the more fissionable U.235 and to use only the latter. For reasons which will become apparent later, this solution, while simple in principle, is extremely difficult in practice. The elegant solution which was considered by Joliot, Fermi and Sir George Thomson aims at by-passing resonance capture without separating the isotopes. If, they argued, ordinary uranium is mixed with a light element, many neutrons will be slowed down by collisions with the nuclei of this light element instead of being captured by U.238. Thus, if the light nuclei are suitably spaced, a fast neutron may not encounter a U.238 nucleus until it has become too slow to be captured and will thereby be preserved for causing fission of U.235. Suitable substances for slowing down neutrons like this are called moderators, and heavy water and carbon have already been mentioned (see chapter 8) in this respect.

We have seen that in order to establish a chain reaction, the number of neutrons causing fission must increase in successive stages or, at least, remain at the same level. If the reaction is to be an explosion, the number of neutrons must increase all the time, comparable with an avalanche of chain letters. Owing to the high energy involved in nuclear reactions, an atomic explosion should be far more effective than an ordinary chemical one; but to ensure its efficiency one more fact has to be considered. A fission bomb, in order to work at all, must have a certain size or else too many neutrons will escape. When such a bomb starts exploding, it may first break up into fragments and in these, because of their smaller size, the reaction will stop. If this is to be prevented the whole reaction must take place with great rapidity and be finished before the fragments have separated. However, the slowing down of neutrons takes time, and calculations showed that no fast explosion could be expected on this basis.

The whole problem was summarized by Frisch in the winter 1939/40 in an article in the Annual Reports of the Chemical Society when he wrote with regard to atomic bombs, "Fortunately our progressing knowledge of the fission process has tended to dissipate these fears and there are now a number of strong arguments to the effect that the construction of such a super bomb would be, if not impossible, then at least prohibitively expensive, and that furthermore the bomb would not be so effective as was thought at first."

For the time it seemed that while it might be possible to release atomic energy in fission by slow neutrons, this release would never take the form of a violent explosion. It seemed as if a provident fate had decreed that only for peaceful ends should man be allowed to lay his hand on the great store of atomic energy. Scientists, and they were then the only ones who could assess the facts, fervently hoped that nuclear explosions might never be possible. However, the time was 1940 and total war had already swept over the plains of Poland. Even in the freedon-loving countries scientists had to face the fact that, if an atomic bomb was possible, it might be used by the enemy and that it would be their duty therefore to investigate all possibilities before they were allowed to shelve the problem.

As everyone knows today, the hope that a nuclear explosion would be impossible was not fulfilled. The official British statement says that: " At the beginning of 1940 Dr. Frisch and Professor Peierls, of Birmingham University, and Professor Sir James Chadwick, of Liverpool University, independently called attention to the possibility of producing a military weapon of unprecedented power." It was known that the isotope U.235 does not only undergo fission if bombarded with slow neutrons but also responds to some extent to fast ones. It could be shown that fission by fast neutrons would probably cause an explosion in uranium from which the U.238 nuclei had mostly been removed. The necessary weight of the bomb was estimated as between one and one hundred kilograms. More data for calculation was certainly needed, but by the summer of 1941 experiments in Liverpool and Cambridge definitely showed that the development of an atomic bomb was feasible provided that a sufficient amount of U.235 could be separated from the rest of the metal.

In the United States too, scientists had persued the question of a nuclear explosion and had reached similar conclusions. It became abundantly clear that, while the production of atomic bombs would involve a major industrial effort, such bombs had a great chance of success. The British as well as the U.S. governments were forced to realise that atomic bombs might be used against them, and that the only possible course was to embark themselves on the project in spite of the heavy commitments this would entail.

The epic story of the development which followed is told in the official statements issued by the British, Canadian and U.S. governments. As these statements emphasize, many facts cannot yet be disclosed for security reasons, but it is to be hoped that in the not too distant future the world will be told the full story of what is without doubt one of the greatest achievements of mankind.

So far our account has only dealt with the nuclear processes underlying the mechanism of a large scale atomic explosion, but nothing has been said about the production of the material for it. Uranium which was discovered in 1789 is a fairly rare substance. It is found in pitchblende, a mineral which until recently was mainly mined at Joachimsthal in Bohemia. Until the discovery of radioactivity, uranium salts in small quantities were used for staining glass and in photography. Early in the century pitchblende acquired a new and important use in the extraction of radium, and a wide search for it and another mineral, carnotite, was begun. The latter was found in some quantity in Colorado and yielded most of the world's radium supply until, in 1923, large amounts of pitchblende began to be mined in the Belgian Congo. Still greater deposits of this mineral were discovered in 1931 by the French-Canadian explorer Gilbert Labine on the east shores of the Great Bear Lake in North Western Canada. These mines which for the greater part of the year are accessible only by air were worked by the Eldorado Mining and Refining Co., until during the war they were taken over by the Dominion Government. It is interesting to note that until 1941 pitchblende and carnotite were worked for radium, uranium being of little interest.

By 1940 it had become clear that the production of atomic bombs depended on the successful extraction of U.235 and this extraction must include two fundamentally different stages of separation. In the first place the element uranium must be separated from the other chemical elements in the mineral ore, and secondly the isotope with the weight 235 must be isolated from the bulk of the substance consisting of atoms with the weight 238. The first process is an ordinary chemical extraction; but the second one, the separation of two isotopes, is necessarily much more difficult and one which up to that time had only been carried out on a large scale in the case of heavy water.

Among isotopes heavy water occupies a unique position

because the weight of the heavy hydrogen atom is twice that of ordinary hydrogen. The difference in weight between U.238 and U.235, on the other hand, only amounts to a little over one per cent and their separation is bound to be much more difficult than that of the hydrogen isotopes. The problem of isotope separation had been solved a long time before fission was discovered and the release of atomic energy was contemplated. A number of different methods for the isolation of rare isotopes had not only been suggested but had actually been operated on the laboratory scale. When in 1939 Urey of Columbia University, one of the foremost experts on the subject, summarised these methods in a scientific report,* he could conclude his survey with the words: "With these methods available it seems that the separation of isotopes in adequate amounts for effective chemical and physical research is solved in principle and only requires persistent effort for actual production."

With the scientific facts available at the end of 1939 it required no specialised knowledge to realise that in the production of a uranium bomb. isotope separation would present by far the largest single item on the bill. The question was therefore not only whether a uranium bomb would work but also whether the material for it could be provided within the existing limits of industrial potential. It seems to be part of the nature of the problem that large scale separation of isotopes is bound to be a slow and costly process which does not offer a simple short cut. The main question which the scientists concerned had to decide was which of the known separation methods should be employed. The fact that a process works successfully on the laboratory scale does not mean that it is suitable for industrial application and it was clearly a task of immense responsibility to determine the best method to which the gigantic industrial effort needed should be applied.

The difference between ordinary chemical separation and isotope separation can be compared with the selection of certain types of people from a crowd. The chemical differences between two substances, depending on the peculiarities

---

* Reports on Progress in Physics, The Physical Society, London, 1939.

of the outermost electrons are reflected in the affinities which
they show towards other substances. Different chemicals,
showing different reactions can be separated fairly easily just
as we can separate men and women by passing them through
a shopping street having men's shops on one side and
women's shops on the other. Isotopes on the other hand
are identical in their chemical behaviour, having the same
outer electron shell. They only differ in the weight of the
nucleus, a difference which does not affect their chemical
affinities. To separate them is somewhat like separating
from a crowd all men weighing less than ten stone. Lightweights do not differ from other men in their habits and
preferences. and it is evident that to sort them out is a very
much harder task than the other separation.

    We can think of two rather different ways of selecting
the lightweights. We can send every man over a trapdoor
which is adjusted to support only weights up to ten stone.
In this way we will achieve " quantitative " separation, but
the process is laborious and will be extremely slow when
large numbers have to be considered. The other way is not
to weigh each man but instead to force large numbers of them
through an obstacle race, in which the lightweights have a
better chance of getting through than the heavy men. This
is a less laborious but certainly not a quantitative method,
since many heavy men will get through the race while there
will be lightweights who will be left behind. In fact all we
can do with this method is to " enrich the concentration " of
the required type of man.

    Both these methods, that corresponding to weighing and
that of the obstacle race have been used in the separation of
U.235. The former corresponds to the electro-magnetic
separator and the latter to the diffusion process. The electro-
magnetic separator is based on Aston's mass spectrograph
which has already been mentioned in connection with the
weight of nuclei. This apparatus makes use of the fact that
a charged particle can be forced into a circular path by the
application of a magnetic field. If all the particles concerned are made to enter the magnetic field with the same
speed, the size of the circles which they describe depends on
their mass, and this therefore offers a possibility of separating

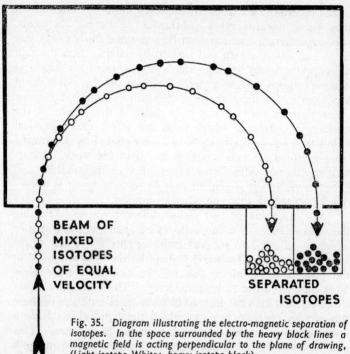

BEAM OF
MIXED
ISOTOPES
OF EQUAL
VELOCITY

SEPARATED
ISOTOPES

Fig. 35. *Diagram illustrating the electro-magnetic separation of isotopes. In the space surrounded by the heavy black lines a magnetic field is acting perpendicular to the plane of drawing, (Light isotope White; heavy isotope black).*

atoms of different weight (plate IX). Thus in a magnetic field a beam of charged atoms splits up into tracks of different curvature which correspond to different weights, and by collecting the atoms at the end of each track, the isotopes can be completely separated. In this way the atoms are weighed by the magnetic field and sorted out according to their mass, like the men passing the trap door. However, unless a very dense beam of atoms is used, the total amount of the required isotope which can be collected is small. Only minute quantities were obtained in Aston's early work; but in 1934 Oliphant and his co-workers were able to obtain appreciable, though still microscopic, quantities of lithium isotopes in this way. In the last few years Lawrence, of the University of

California and Oliphant with their teams of co-workers have
carried out large scale separation of the uranium isotopes.
In order to obtain the necessary amount of U.235 within a
reasonable time, a large number of such electro-magnetic
separation units had to be operated simultaneously.   A suitable design had been worked out at the California laboratory
by 1943 and in April of that year a proto-type unit was
operating there.   Six months later the electro-magnetic
separation plant at the Clinton Engineer Works in Tennessee
began to produce batches of U.235.   This was the first large
scale production of U.235.

The diffusion process is based on the fact that heavier
atoms are less mobile than lighter ones.   When a stream of
gas is passed through narrow channels, as for instance in a
porous filter, the lighter isotope stands a better chance of
getting through than the heavier one.   Behind the filter,

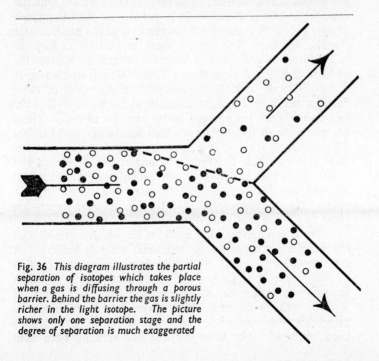

Fig. 36 This diagram illustrates the partial
separation of isotopes which takes place
when a gas is diffusing through a porous
barrier. Behind the barrier the gas is slightly
richer in the light isotope.   The picture
shows only one separation stage and the
degree of separation is much exaggerated

therefore the gas will be richer in the lighter isotope. Of course, as with our analogy of men being put through an obstacle race, a lot of heavy atoms will get through and a lot of light ones will stay behind. The process can be varied in a great many ways but always a partial separation only will be attained. Only by passing the gas through a great many filters can an isotope be obtained in good purity.

In 1932 Hertz in Berlin successfully used the diffusion method for the separation of neon isotopes on a laboratory scale, but the large scale separation of the uranium isotopes presented formidable difficulties. In order to use the method, a gaseous uranium compound must be chosen and it is clear that the handling of large quantities of such a gas would be especially troublesome if the gas were corrosive. The number of diffusion stages must be very great if a high degree of separation is required. It has been estimated that, using the gas uranium hexafluoride, altogether 4000 stages are required in order to obtain U.235 of 99% purity. In turn thousands of pumps of high capacity are needed to feed the gas from one stage to another. The porous filters, or barriers as they are called, must be uniform and must not contain an appreciable number of holes of more than 1/2,000,000 inch in diameter.

In a large scale separation plant many acres of these barriers are needed and provision must be made so that the fine holes do not get plugged up by particles of dust. These are just some of the problems which had to be solved before diffusion separation of the uranium isotopes was possible. Research into these questions was undertaken by Simon and Peierls in Britain and by Urey and Dunning in America, and in 1943 the first large scale tests were undertaken in pilot plants. In the summer of 1945 the big diffusion separation plant at Clinton was started up (plate III).

These are not the only methods by which separation of the uranium isotopes on an industrial scale is feasible. A centrifuge, for instance, will also produce separation according to weight and it is known that in an enclosure in which a temperature difference is set up, a partial separation of isotopes will be effected. Pilot plants based on these two principles were applied to the isolation of U.235 and have been operated. The latter method has actually been used to supply uranium enriched in U.235 for use in the electro-magnetic separation plant.

With a suitable scheme for the nuclear reaction and with the separation of U.235 on an industrial scale, the problem of the atomic bomb is by no means settled. Many other scientific and technical questions had to be solved before such a bomb could be constructed, and in 1943 a special laboratory for the investigation of these problems was set up under the direction of J. R. Oppenheimer of the University of California. For reasons of safety and secrecy an isolated site at Los Alamos 30 miles from Santa Fe in New Mexico was chosen for this work.

It is obvious that pure U.235, once it has been separated may be an extremely dangerous substance to handle. The fission of uranium nuclei is caused by their meeting with a neutron. Neutrons on the other hand pass easily through matter and it seems therefore quite impossible to guard a piece of uranium completely against stray neutrons, particu-larly since occasionally neutrons are even liberated in the metal itself by spontaneous fission of a nucleus. On the other hand, as we have seen, a piece of U.235 which is small enough will not explode even under neutron bombardment, because too many neutrons escape from it. In such a small piece there will be very little chance of one of the liberated neutrons hitting another nucleus before escaping from the substance. Even if by a rare chance one of these neutrons hits another nucleus, the neutrons from this second fission will certainly get away without doing any harm.

However, the more U.235 nuclei that are collected in one lump, the greater will be the chance of the first neutron encountering and setting off a second nucleus and of the secondary neutrons then produced setting off further nuclei, and so on. In short, one must at some stage in the process of collecting U.235 arrive at a lump of such a size that no neutron is likely to escape out of it without exploding the whole lump. A lump of U.235 greater than this " critical " size therefore can never exist at all. On the other hand a lump considerably smaller than the critical size will be safe to handle. An accurate prediction of this critical size was one of the prerequisites of the development of the bomb, and this

clearly entailed careful measurements of physical data concerning the fission process as well as laborious and difficult
calculations. Because of the existence of a critical size, a
nuclear explosion cannot be tested out on a small sample of
explosive, and experiments of a different nature had to be
devised in order to check the calculations. Among the test
experiments listed in the Smyth report is one in which a
chain reaction in uranium was set up with the help of a
moderator. As has already been mentioned such a device
will decrease the speed of neutrons, and the reaction is one
in which fission is caused by slow neutrons. In a series of
successive experiments, the amount of moderator used was
gradually decreased and the reaction took up more and more
the character of a fast neutron chain such as happens in the
bomb.

The existence of a critical size also suggests a method
for the detonation of an atomic bomb. If the bomb consists
of two or more pieces of the nuclear explosive, each below the
critical size, they will be safe as long as they remain apart.
However, as soon as they are brought together, the critical
size is exceeded and they will explode. It is clear that the
reaction may begin before the pieces actually touch, and in
order to secure an effective explosion they must be brought
together very rapidly. One of the methods suggested to
achieve this, is to shoot a piece of nuclear explosive into
another by means of a gun.

The critical size of a lump of U.235 can be reduced by
surrounding it with a material which will reflect the escaping
neutrons back into the explosive. Such a device is called a
tamper, and besides decreasing the size it can have the effect
of keeping the bomb fragments together long enough for a
fair proportion of the explosive to undergo fission. It will
be remembered that there is a danger that the reaction may
stop too early because individual fragments may be produced
each of which is below the critical size.

A trial bomb was exploded on July 16th 1945, in the New
Mexican Desert. The test was most successful, resulting in
a blast wave of extreme force. Those who were present
mention in particular the enormous luminosity of the phenomenon which is caused by the intense heat of the explosion.

At the moment of detonation the atoms of matter concerned in it will acquire tremendous speed, and the centre of the explosion will therefore be extremely hot, probably many million degrees, and will for a short time send out energy not only as blast, that is by outward movement of matter, but also in the form of radiation (plates X and XI).

The scale of destruction caused in Japan shows that the blast of an atomic bomb will wipe out 10 square miles of a city. To achieve the same result with ordinary explosives, about 1,000 2-ton block busters are required. The effect of radiation which in ordinary bombs is quite negligible is pronounced and the radiated heat causes fires and produces severe burns. People within several hundred yards of the explosion were charred black, while others further away were fatally burnt by ultra-violet rays. Added to this is the effect of gamma radiation which kills the white blood corpuscles and destroys the ability of the blood to clot, thereby causing blood to seep through the body and the skin. Damage to tissues, particularly the blood producing ones, caused many delayed deaths. The total number of deaths at Hiroshima was of the order of 100,000. It was evidently in anticipation of these results that two months before Hiroshima a committee of scientists under the chairmanship of James Franck had urged the U.S. Secretary of War to demonstrate to Japan the effect of the bomb in an uninhabited locality.

Atomic energy has stepped into the world of human affairs as a child of man's ingenuity. It is idle to speculate whether it would have been better if this new and powerful agent had for ever been withheld from our grasp. The clock cannot be turned back. It is up to the men and woman of all nations to see that atomic energy, which has come into man's hand as a weapon of destruction, is developed as an aid to peace and prosperity.

In view of the great amount of scientific fact which was known before bomb development started and in the face of the information disclosed by the official statements, the reader will ask what then is the much discussed secret of the atomic bomb, or as the more sensational reports say: "the secret formula." To anyone who is familiar with the vicissitudes of scientific research and technical development it is clear that,

even with all the fundamental facts known, there must have
been literally hundreds of subsidiary problems to be solved.
Some of these will have concerned the accurate determination
of physical data while most of them are likely to have been of
a technical character. It is fairly easy to set out the fundamental physical principles according to which a motor car
works; it is quite a different matter to build one and make it
run   It is more than probable that the remaining secret of the
atomic bomb like that of any great technical development is
vested in the experience of scientists and technicians which
has been acquired in years of hard work. The greatest of all
secrets certainly is out: The atomic bomb works! Anyone
embarking on its manufacture now, is fortified with this
knowledge.

It is a debatable point whether processes of manufacture
ought to be kept secret or not, but such secrecy is by no
means confined to the making of atomic bombs. It is a
different question whether fundamental scientific discoveries
ought to be kept secret. Most scientists will agree that
secrecy in this respect is not only undesirable but futile. If
Hahn and Strassmann had kept the discovery of fission a
secret, somebody else would have discovered it soon enough.
The history of science shows that in spite of apparent
" accidents," progress can only be achieved in a methodical
manner, and when the requisite state of knowledge has been
reached certain discoveries are bound to be made. Four
hundred years ago the powers of the day tried to hide the
discovery that the earth spins round the sun. Nevertheless
the secret has leaked out in the course of time and is known
to every schoolchild today.

CHAPTER TEN

CONTROLLED RELEASE

THE furious blast of an atomic bomb, although an extremely impressive release of energy, seems hardly amenable to utilisation in a power plant. In the past twenty yeors it was often said that atomic energy, even if it could be released, would hardly be of use because of the extreme temperatures generated. It might be presumed that nuclear changes, such as take place in the interior of the stars, could not be managed on the earth except in violent explosions. This is, however, not quite true. The alpha-particles set free from the radio-active material on the luminous dial of a watch have a speed corresponding to a temperature of many million degrees and yet cause no discomfort to the owner. In a lump of uranium, the fission products fly apart with an energy of motion corresponding to a million million degrees, but this is not the temperature of the whole piece unless all the atoms undergo fission at the same instant. The temperature of a body at any time is given by the *average* energy of motion of the atoms of which the body is composed. When a uranium nucleus undergoes fission, the two fragments flying apart with great energy do not retain their energy of motion for long. They collide with other uranium atoms, and share their energy with them. Thus shortly after fission has taken place there are instead of the two fragments with high energy, many atoms with a slightly increased energy. In effect the lump of uranium becomes a little warmer.

The temperature which is generated in a body has, therefor, little to do with the energy of each individual reaction but depends rather on the *rate* at which this energy is released. When a uranium atom breaks up in fission it releases about 30 million times more energy than that released by a carbon atom undergoing ordinary combustion. Therefore, if energy is to be delivered at the same steady rate from a uranium source as from the burning of a lump of coal,

30 million times as many carbon atoms as uranium nuclei will have to undergo reaction in each minute. In other words, there is no fundamental difference between an atomic energy source and the burning of coal, except that in order to generate the same power output, uranium nuclei need only be used up at a rate 30 million times slower than carbon atoms.

The difference in applicability of the two power sources on the other hand becomes apparent when it is remembered that a lump of coal holds roughly the same number of atoms as a lump of uranium of similar size. Considering therefore bulk or weight of fuel, uranium is 30 million times more concentrated than coal. It has thus to be admitted that nuclear reactions are particularly suited to produce explosions because they allow a *concentration* of energy in a given space or weight 10 million times higher than in a chemical explosive. Besides its destructive use in atomic bombs, nuclear fission will most likely be adopted in the future as the source of power in ships or in aircraft of long endurance where small weight of fuel is essential. This will, of course, depend on whether it is possible to devise power units which are sufficiently simple and small so as not to nullify the advantage of a concentrated fuel.

When on 16th July 1945 the trial atomic bomb exploded, it was not the first release of atomic energy achieved by man. Two and a half years previously a peculiar installation had been erected in a squash court underneath the grand stand of the Chicago stadium, and on 2nd December 1942 this apparatus began to deliver atomic energy in a smooth and steady stream. In order to understand and appreciate this earlier development we must return to the problems which were current in the days when nuclear fission was discovered.

The discovery of fission seemed to provide a full explanation of the great number of strange results which had been obtained by Fermi and others in the five years preceding it. It will be remembered that, instead of one or two new "transuranic" elements which should have made their appearance when uranium was bombarded by neutrons, a great number were found. After Hahn and Strassmann published their results on barium, it was generally assumed that *all* these new nuclei were not transuranic ones but were radio-active isotopes of much lighter elements. They were clearly the fragments of uranium nuclei which had undergone fission. Nevertheless it soon became apparent that the process which Fermi originally foresaw does actually take place. The uranium nuclei which break up under neutron bombardment are mostly those of U.235, whereas the nuclei of U.238 tend to retain the neutrons which hit them and change into U.239. In fact, it was just this resonance capture of neutrons which prohibited a chain reaction in ordinary uranium and which necessitated the separation of U.235 for the atomic bomb. The question that remained therefore was, what happens to the nuclei of U.239?

The answer was given by experiments carried out with the big cyclotron at the University of California, particularly by McMillan and Abelson. The most important of the results obtained was the discovery of two new transuranic elements to which the names neptunium and plutonium have been given. The nucleus U.239 turned out to be rather unstable, having a half life time of only 23 minutes. It emits an electron and its atomic number is thus increased to 93. The new element, neptunium, thus created lives for a little over two days and then emits an electron, becoming plutonium with atomic number 94. Thus after seven years of disappointments and surprises, Fermi's original idea was proved correct. The two new elements with higher atomic numbers than uranium, must have existed in a bygone phase of the universe and have died out long since. In our time they have been re-created artificially in the laboratory.

Plutonium appears to be a fairly stable substance. It has a half life time of 34,000 years*. In its chemical

---

* A number of transuranic nuclei, other than those mentioned above, have also been discovered. Bombardment of U.238 with deuterons produces $^{238}_{93}$Np, which, after emitting an electron turns into $^{238}_{94}$Pu, a plutonium isotope with a half life of about 50 years. Neutron bombardment of U.238 results occasionally in the re-emission of two neutrons and the formation of U.237 which, by electron emission, produces $^{273}_{93}$Np. This neptunium isotope has a very long half life (2,250,000 years). Finally, Seaborg has recently announced the discovery of elements 95 and 96, as yet unnamed. Chemically these elements, as well as neptunium and plutonium, much resemble uranium, and it is likely that the new electrons which are being added to the electronic cloud at each step are not placed in the outermost layer but are accommodated in a lower shell (see appendix 2).

behaviour plutonium is rather similar to uranium but differs sufficiently to enable it to be separated from uranium by chemical methods which, as we shall presently see, is a most important point. Plutonium ($^{239}_{49}$Pu) created considerable interest even before it was discovered. Predictions as to the behaviour of hypothetical transuranic nuclei had been made both by Bohr and Wheeler and by Turner of Princeton. From these considerations it followed that the yet unknown nucleus with atomic number 94 and weight 239 might be expected to resemble U.235 to some extent as far as fission was concerned.

The results obtained in California, showing that transuranic elements could indeed be built up, opened entirely new prospects for the release of atomic energy. It has to be recalled that in 1939 a number of physicists pointed out the possibility of attaining a slow neutron chain reaction with the use of a moderator. The idea of this scheme was to use ordinary uranium and to preserve a sufficient number of neutrons to ensure fission of the U.235 contained in it. This was to be achieved by by-passing resonance capture. Because of the time taken by the reaction, this scheme proved useless for atomic bombs, nevertheless it is exactly what is required for the production of plutonium. Provided just enough neutrons are preserved to keep the reaction going in it, one can allow all other neutrons to be captured by U.238 which will then turn into plutonium. The prospects were summarized in 1941 by E. O. Lawrence in a report (quoted in the Smyth statement) in which he said:

" It appears accordingly that, if a chain reaction with unseparated isotopes is achieved, it may be allowed to proceed violently for a period of time for the express purpose of manufacturing element 94 in substantial amounts. This material could be extracted by ordinary chemistry and would presumably be the equivalent of uranium 235 for chain reaction purposes.

" If this is so, the following three outstanding important possibilities are opened:

"" 1.   Uranium 238 would be available for energy production, thus increasing about one hundred fold the total atomic energy available from a given quantity of uranium.

" 2.   Using element 94 one may envisage preparation of small chain reaction units for power purposes weighing perhaps a hundred pounds instead of a hundred tons as probably would be necessary for units using natural uranium.

" 3.   If large amounts of element 94 were available it is likely that a chain reaction with fast neutrons could be produced. In such a reaction the energy would be released at an explosive rate which might be described as a super bomb."

With the world at war, the last possibility mentioned by Lawrence had to be given foremost consideration.   Here was a new nuclear explosive which could be extracted by chemical means, avoiding the laborious isotope separation.   However, before this substance could be obtained, a nuclear chain reaction had to be set going.   Eighteen months later this was done.   There is poetical justice in the fact that it was Fermi who achieved the first manufacture of those transuranic elements in search of which he had set out eight years before. In due course, the U.S. Government authorized the building of a large plant for the production of plutonium at Hanford near Pasco, Washington, which began to operate in September 1944.   It was an early prototype of this plant which first liberated atomic energy one year after Pearl Harbour.

In all this work, the only object was the manufacture of plutonium for use in atomic bombs, and the atomic energy liberated in the process was therefore considered an encumberance and not an asset.   In fact, much ingenuity had to be displayed in devising means of getting rid of the unwanted power.   Nevertheless the production of plutonium is a highlight in the short history of atomic energy, not only because of the extreme elegance of the scientific solution but also because the method developed shows how atomic energy can be released at any desired rate.   This is how it works:

The fast neutrons liberated by fission in a piece of ordinary uranium are nearly all consumed by resonance capture in U.238 as soon as they have lost some of their speed.   There may be however a few neutrons which have been slowed down to very small velocities and which have escaped capture and these stand a high chance of causing fission of the U.235 nuclei.   When a neutron is slowed down it reaches finally a limiting velocity below which it cannot go.

This limiting slow speed is given when in its collisions with other nuclei energy is exchanged equally between them. Speaking in terms of heat, we can say that these neutrons have the same temperature as the lump of uranium in which they live and they are called therefore " thermal neutrons." A thermal neutron is too slow to penetrate into a U.238 nucleus and get captured so that although it collides with many of them it always bounces off without reacting. Wandering in this way to and fro through the lump of uranium the neutron will eventually meet a U.235 nucleus and set it off in fission. Only one nucleus in every 140 is a U.235, but since the thermal neutron cannot react with the other nuclei, it is bound to find its mark in the end. When it breaks up the U.235 nucleus in fission, new neutrons are produced.

These neutrons emanating from fission have a high speed and they present a suitable prey for the U.238 nuclei. One to three neutrons are produced in each fission and consequently if a chain reaction shall result, at least one of these neutrons must be preserved to initiate another fission. It must be slowed down without being caught. As we have seen before, this condition is not fufilled in a lump of ordinary uranium. The table on page 140 shows that the real danger for the neutron occurs when it has a medium velocity, corresponding to the resonance level of the U.238 nucleus. Once it has been slowed down below this dangerous speed, it is quite safe. The critical period in a neutron's life is somewhat similar to that for young people who are especially prone to form undesirable attachments at a certain age. Careful parents will see to it that at this susceptible age, the young ones are kept away from unsuitable friendships.

Much the same method has been adopted with regard to the fast neutrons. The uranium is dispersed in a moderator, an innocuous substance, with which neutrons do not form attachments of any sort. All that can happen to them in it, is to suffer collisions and get slower. Thus, if uranium is sufficiently salted with this moderator, most of the fast neutrons newly created by fission will never have the chance to meet a dangerous U.238 while they are still fast enough to be captured. When however they are at last tired and slow, occasional collisions with U.238 nuclei will have no

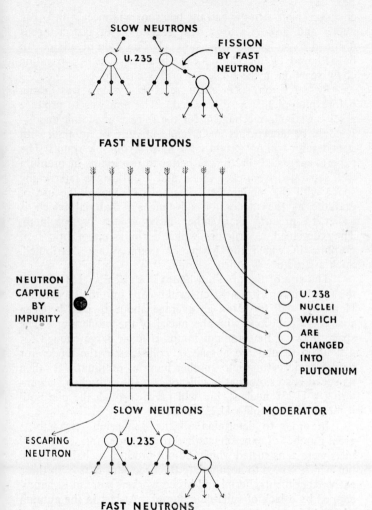

SLOW NEUTRONS

U. 235

FISSION
BY FAST
NEUTRON

FAST NEUTRONS

FAST NEUTRONS

NEUTRON
CAPTURE
BY
IMPURITY

U. 238
NUCLEI
WHICH
ARE
CHANGED
INTO
PLUTONIUM

SLOW NEUTRONS

MODERATOR

ESCAPING
NEUTRON

U. 235

FAST NEUTRONS

Fig. 37. *Diagram of the processes which go on in a plutonium pile.   It will be noticed that the number of fissions in successive stages is the same.   This means that the reaction will proceed at a fixed power level.*

effect on them.   In the end the neutrons will meet with U.235 nuclei and give rise to a new generation of fast neutrons destined to suffer the same fate.   If this state of affairs can be achieved by the careful experimenter, a self-propagating chain reaction in the nuclear world is ensured.

Research on such chain reaction systems was begun before plutonium was discovered.   The aim was to produce a self-sustaining mechanism for the release of atomic energy. It could be shown that an intimate mixture of uranium with a moderator will not produce the most favourable results. The experts suggested that it was better to use lumps of uranium well separated from each other, and to fill up the intervening space with the moderator.   They also proposed the use of graphite as the moderator substance, a material which is easier to procure than either heavy water or beryllium. They designed a structure which is built up of bricks of graphite in which the lumps of uranium are distributed. Such a structure is called a " pile."

The size of the uranium lumps is chosen so that most of the fast neutrons from fissions will escape into the moderator. Here they will travel on an average about an inch between successive collisions with the nuclei of the moderator.   The space between the uranium lumps is made large enough for a neutron to undergo about 200 collisions in the moderator before again getting into another lump of uranium.   By then its speed is so slow that it will not be captured when encountering a U.238 nucleus, but will move through the pile until it meets and sets off a U.235 nucleus.

In order to determine all the dimensions correctly a great number of experiments had to be made, and some small piles were constructed which did not produce a chain reaction but which served to accumulate the necessary data.   In these early experiments, Fermi and his co-workers were most handicapped by a lack of suitable material.   At last in the autumn of 1942, 6 tons of uranium metal and a sufficient quantity of pure graphite were available to build a proper chain-reaction pile.   The description given in the Smyth report shows that when finished the structure had the shape of a flattened sphere, looking rather like a door knob.   Between the graphite blocks a number of gaps were left into which instruments and control gear could be pushed. As early as 1939 Adler and von Halban, as well as Perrin, had suggested that strips of cadmium metal which effectively stops the passage of neutrons through them, could be used to regulate a nuclear chain-reacting system. Such control strips were placed into this first full scale pile and worked very well.

The analogy of the chain letters which has been discussed before has shown that in order to keep the process going, at least as many letters must be written in each stage as have been written in the preceding one. The number of free and slowly moving neutrons in a pile such as are needed to cause fission depends not only on the successful by-passing of the " dangerous " velocity but also on the ease with which neutrons can escape out of the whole system. As in a piece of uranium, the chance of escape becomes smaller as the pile grows in size. The method adopted with the first pile therefore was to build it up gradually and to measure the number of neutrons produced by fission as the structure increased in size. In this way it was possible to predict accurately when the critical size would be reached. This critical size is the minimum size which must be reached in order to make the reaction self-propagating. In actual fact, the pile was increased to a slightly larger size but the number of fissions was purposely kept down by the insertion of control strips. In this way, the rate of production of energy could be changed at will by moving a control strip just as the rate of combustion in a boiler can be regulated by means of a damper. When the damper is pulled out, the increased air supply stimulates combustion, causing in turn more draught until the whole system adjusts itself to a new and higher rate of energy production. Similarly, removal of cadmium strips in a pile produces a higher number of fissions and more secondary neutrons until the system settles down to a steady rate of production of energy which is higher than the original one.

The operation of a pile is greatly helped by a peculiarity of the fission process. It was noticed early in the work that not all neutrons are produced instantaneously at the moment of fission. A few are emitted from the fission products several seconds or even a minute after the actual fission has taken place. This lag in neutron production is very welcome because it make for gradualness in the changes in power production that follow a new setting of the controls. In fact, the report indicates that the running of an atomic energy pile is by no means a hectic occupation. Even an automatic regulator was attached to this first pile which would push in. a control strip when the set power level was exceeded. The pile furthermore could be shut down completely by putting in a number of cadmium strips.

The total power dissipated in the pile was at first half a watt and this was increased ten days later to 200 watts. Running at this rate for the production of plutonium, the pile would only furnish sufficient material for a bomb every 100,000 years or so. It is evident therefore that piles must be operated at a very much higher power level if appreciable amounts of plutonium are to be manufactured. However, it proved impracticable to raise the output of this first pile because of the harmful radiation which it was likely to produce. The use of radioactive materials on a large industrial scale provides peculiar and serious problems of its own.

By the time the first pile was operating, the production of plutonium had become the main purpose of such systems involving slow neutron reactions. A neutron freshly liberated by fission in a chain-reacting pile is faced by a number of eventualities. It may be slowed down and cause fission of a nucleus or, in rare cases, it may cause fission before being slowed down. It may be captured and thus produce plutonium. Finally it may escape or be captured by impurities. The processes which compete for the neutron in a pile are therefore the same as those which must be considered in an atomic bomb. The difference is that, while in a bomb all other processes except fission are undesirable, in a pile a balance must be struck between fission and resonance capture. Escape and capture by impurities must, of course, be kept down both in a pile and in a bomb. In practice it turns out that in a pile resonance capture is always so pronounced that there is little chance of having too many neutrons left over to cause fission.

In a pile for the production of plutonium, the processed metal has to be extracted from the structure from time to time and replaced by fresh uranium metal. The arrangement used in the first pile, in which the metal was distributed in isolated lumps throughout the moderator bricks, was very unsuitable for a production unit. In the large pile built at Clinton uranium rods were used and the whole pile was shaped like a cube. This pile began to work in November 1943. Producing power at a rate of 800 kilowatts, the uranium in it took up a temperature of only 150° centigrade. The power level in it has since been increased to over 1800 kilowatts.

This pile served as a pilot unit for the big production plant at Hanford (plate III) which in 1945 had three piles in operation. These work at a very high power level, producing every day a few grams of plutonium per ton of uranium metal in the pile. As the reaction goes on, both U.238 and U.235 are used up, and whereas there is an almost inexhaustible supply of the former, a time must come when the small stock of U.235 contained in the metal becomes depleted. However, as U.235 is used up by fission, fresh fissionable material in the form of newly formed plutonium makes its appearance in the pile. In this way the reaction could proceed for a very long time, continually producing both energy and plutonium, were it not for the fission fragments. The breaking up of each heavy nucleus, U.235 or plutonium, gives birth to two atoms of roughly half the weight. The longer the pile is in operation, the greater will be the number of these nuclei, which thus contaminate the uranium metal increasingly. Impurities as has been mentioned, impair the proper functioning of the chain reaction because they capture neutrons, and these artificially produced impurities are no exception. Accordingly, after the pile has been running for some time the " poisoning " effect of the fission products becomes so strong that the metal has to be extracted and the pile stocked with new uranium.

The extraction of the processed metal from the pile has to be carried out under stringent precautions. The first small pile operating in a Chicago squash court had to be limited to a power level of 200 watts because of the danger from radiation. The Clinton pile operates at a power level 10,000 times as high and the power level of the Hanford piles is probably still higher. It is clear that these structures must •

be very powerful sources of radiation, and they are therefore surrounded by thick walls of steel or concrete. All operations on them are carried out by remote control. The processed metal extracted from the pile is intensely radioactive and cannot be handled directly. It is transferred under water to the chemical separation plant where it is dissolved. Extraction, transfer and chemical separation, even the necessary chemical analyses, have to be done by remote control. The separated plutonium metal is not dangerously radioactive, but the disposal of the fission fragments requires careful attention. Insufficient dispersal of radioactive waste products can seriously affect life in the neighbourhood of a plutonium plant. In particular, two of the fission products, radioactive iodine and xenon, are gases which, unless special precautions are taken, are liable to escape easily from the separation process.

From a large plutonium pile thousands of kilowatts of unwanted atomic energy have to be removed. This is done by water cooling, the required water supply equalling that of a whole town. In the case of the Hanford piles, water is taken from the Columbia river, heated in the pile and then returned to the river. However, when passing through the pile, the cooling water becomes radioactive and has subsequently to be passed into a retention basin, in which its radioactivity dies down in time, before it can be returned to the river.

All reactions between atomic nuclei are accompanied by radiation which to a greater or lesser extent is detrimental to health. Special precautions must therefore be taken with regard to all personnel engaged in this kind of work. Similar problems have arisen before in hospitals where radium and x-ray therapy are used extensively, and the methods for protection employed in atomic energy laboratories and plants have been developed on the lines of the hospital technique. The trouble with these radiations is that they are insidious; their effect is not noted instantaneously and they cannot be seen. All workers therefore are made to carry small recording indicators, electroscopes or photographic film, which are checked weekly. These and other precautions have met with excellent success in the work on the atomic bomb. New techniques bring new problems, and the atomic industry is very young indeed. It is only just fifty years ago that Becquerel saw the first faint imprint of radioactivity on a photographic plate.

Physics has gone a long way in these fifty years, and we do not know where the next step will lead us. Becquerel could not forsee that within the life of a generation the faint rays from his crystal would lead to one of the gravest problems in the history of mandkind. Today when we are burdened with the heavy responsibility which scientific progress has placed upon our shoulders it is well to take a balanced view of what has been achieved and what remains to be done. What prospect does atomic energy hold for us in war and peace?

So far the outstanding feature is not the total amount of energy which has been released in the atomic bomb but rather the enormous concentration of energy. As regards the scale of destruction, Hiroshima and Nagasaki are eclipsed by the destruction of the Ruhr and the German cities, achieved by the use of ordinary high explosive. The sudden large scale havoc which can be caused by a single plane dropping atomic bombs is terrifying in the extreme, but it remains an open question whether the destruction caused by ordinary chemical energy in this war could have been achieved at a smaller cost in money by the use of atomic energy. It is a sad reflection that we do not count the expense when we set out to kill each other but are inclined to be extremely careful with money when we help each other to live. In short, atomic power may be worth having in war but it may not pay its way in peace, except for special purposes.

All stores of energy are locked, and work must be expended before energy is released. Coal has to be mined before it can be burned and U.235 has to be separated before it can be exploded. The question thus is: Will in future the release of one kilowatt-hour of atomic energy be cheaper than the release of one kilowatt-hour derived from coal or petrol? It is doubtful whether this question can be answered at present but it would seem that the energy release in plutonium production may have certain advantages compared with the separation of U.235. In the case of the former, both processes, fission of U.235 and fission of plutonium, occur spontaneously with release of energy. A plutonium pile can be made to produce plutonium and provide power, and the gained plutonium can then be fissioned in a controlled chain reaction, yielding more power. On the other hand, raw materials of great purity and high running cost are involved.

While it cannot be denied that, because of its very great concentration of energy, atomic power is particularly suited to the destructive uses of war, yet it is bound to have most important peace time applications. Some of these have been briefly mentioned earlier in this chapter, many others will suggest themselves in time to come. Atomic energy may enable man to embark on projects which so far have remained dreams and fairy tales. Perhaps it will place at our disposal a means of penetrating into space or of breaking up hurricanes. However, for the present the peoples of the world are more concerned with abolishing the threat of its destructive power. Effective control of atomic energy is in the first place not a problem of science but one of international politics. Science, however, can play its part in making this control feasible.

The world wide use of atomic explosives must necessarily constitute a constant source of danger. Should some of these explosives come into the hands of ruthless political adventurers, the end of our civilisation will be near. Scientists have therefore proposed that fissionable materials should only be made available in non-explosive form which, however, is suitable for power production. In order to be explosive, plutonium and U.235 must have a certain degree of purity; impurities will capture neutrons and make an explosive chain reaction impossible. On the other hand, atomic energy can be obtained, as we have seen, from a mixture of U.235 and U.238 by means of a pile. Thus, the fissionable substance can yield its atomic energy even if it contains "wrong" atoms, but it will not be explosive. A pound of U.235 contains the *same* amount of energy whether it is pure or, as in ordinary uranium, dispersed in a great mass of U.238. The difference is that, whereas in the first case this energy can be liberated in the fraction of a second, it can only be released relatively slowly in the impure material. The only safeguard is therefore to " denature " all fissionable materials for power production, that means to make them safe against use in bombs, shells or rockets. The denaturing process will consist in mixing the atomic explosive with a sufficient number of " wrong " atoms, and in order to be effective the resultant mixture must be highly inseparable. We have seen earlier that, while any mixture of different chemical elements can be separated without very great difficulty, a mixture of isotopes of the same element presents a much knottier problem. Effective denaturation of fissionable material will therefore be achieved by diluting it with an isotope of the same element which, however, does not undergo fission itself and which captures neutrons. A safeguard of this kind will not, of course, make political control unnecessary but it will make it much easier. Separation for the purposes of war of the denatured material requires large and expensive plants which at present cannot be erected in less than a year. Even so, rigid international supervision of all atomic energy installations and, above all, of the production centres of fissionable materials is an essential pre-requisite for the world wide peaceful application of atomic power. Once this control, based on mutual confidence and respect among the nations, is brought into being, mankind can look forward to enjoying the benefits which a new and great source power is bound to bestow upon it.

However, it is not only the economic issue that matters. It is not the question of whether in 20 years time atomic energy will have cheapened the cost of electric light that should set us thinking. When the men of the Renaissance set out on great voyages of discovery, it was not merely in search of gold and spices. There are periods in the history of mankind, when it reaches out beyond the confines of the known world. Bartholomeo Diaz, Christopher Columbus and the men who sailed with them to what might have been the end of the world did not do it merely to grow rich. Men of their calibre could have made money more easily and safely at home. They set out into the unknown because they wanted to see what was beyond the horizon. Their time was great but it was not easy. Only the glory is remembered, their wars and misery are forgotten. Today again man's mind reaches out into new and undiscovered territory but for most of us the view is obscured by our daily worries and our weariness. Let us now and then forget the troubles and tribulations of our time and see its greatness. Let us rejoice that we in our lifetime are privileged to witness one of the most glorious achievements in the history of mankind.

APPENDIX.

(1) List of the Chemical Elements.

Atomic Number	Symbol	Name	Atomic Number	Symbol	Name
1	H	Hydrogen	48	Cd	Cadmium
2	He	Helium	49	In	Indium
3	Li	Lithium	50	Sn	Tin
4	Be	Beryllium	51	Sb	Antimony
5	B	Boron	52	Te	Tellurium
6	C	Carbon	53	I	Iodine
7	N	Nitrogen	54	Xe	Xenon
8	O	Oxygen	55	Cs	Caesium
9	F	Fluorine	56	Ba	Barium
10	Ne	Neon	57	La	Lanthanum
11	Na	Sodium	58	Ce	Cerium
12	Mg	Magnesium	58	Pr	Phraseodymium
13	Al	Aluminium	60	Nd	Neodymium
14	Si	Silicon	61	—	
15	P	Phosphorus	62	Sm	Samarium
16	S	Sulphur	63	Eu	Europium
17	Cl	Chlorine	64	Gd	Gadolinium
18	A	Argon	65	Tb	Terbium
19	K	Potassium	66	Dy	Dysprosium
20	Ca	Calcium	67	Ho	Holmium
21	Sc	Scandium	68	Er	Erbium
22	Ti	Titanium	69	Tm	Thulium
23	V	Vanadium	70	Yb	Ytterbium
24	Cr	Chromium	71	Lu	Lutecium
25	Mn	Manganese	72	Hf	Hafnium
26	Fe	Iron	73	Ta	Tantalum
27	Co	Cobalt	74	W	Tungsten
28	Ni	Nickel	75	Re	Rhenium
29	Cu	Copper	76	Os	Osmium
30	Cn	Zinc	77	Ir	Iridium
31	Ga	Gallium	78	Pt	Platinum
32	Ge	Germanium	79	Au	Gold
33	As	Arsenic	80	Hg	Mercury
34	Se	Selenium	81	Tl	Thallium
35	Br	Bromine	82	Pb	Lead
36	Kr	Krypton	83	Bi	Bismuth
37	Rb	Rubidium	84	Po	Polonium
38	Sr	Strontium	85	—	
39	Y	Yttrium	86	Rn	Radon
40	Zr	Zirconium	87	—	
41	Nb	Niobium	88	Ac	Radium
42	Mo	Molybdenum	89	Ac	Actinium
43	—		90	Th	Thorium
44	Ru	Ruthenium	91	Pa	Protactinium
45	Rh	Rhodium	92	U	Uranium
46	Pd	Palladium	(93	Np	Neptunium)
47	Ag	Silver	(94	Pu	Plutonium)

(2) The Periodic Table of Elements.

The elements are arranged according to their atomic number.

The horizontal lines represent successive electron shells and elements in the same vertical column have similar chemical properties. In the string of elements surrounded by black lines the added electrons are not placed in the outermost shell but are accommodated in a lower shell. The outer electron shells of these elements and their chemical properties are therefore very similar.

H ————————————————————————————— He Helium

Li Be ————————————— B C N O F Ne Neon shell

Na Mg ———————————— Al Si P S Cl A Argon shell

K Ca Sc ———— Ti V Cr Mn Fe Co Ni Cu Zn Ga Ge As Se Br Kr Krypton shell

Rb Sr Y ———— Zr Nb Mo 43 Ru Rh Pd Ag Cd In Sn Sb Te I Xe Xenon shell

Cs Ba La | Ce Pr Nd 61 Sm Eu Gd Tb Dy Ho Er Tm Yb Lu | Hf Ta W Re Os Ir Pt Au Hg Tl Pb Bi Po 85 Rn Radon shell

87 Ra Ac | Th Pa U Np Pu 95 96 | unfinished shell

APPENDIX   171

(3) The 3 Radioactive Families.

Uranium series	Thorium series	Actinium series
$^{238}_{92}$U(a)	$^{232}_{90}$Th(a)	$^{235}_{92}$U(a)
4400 million y	18000 million y	400 million y
↓	↓	↓
$^{234}_{90}$UX$_1$(b)	$^{228}_{88}$MsTh$_1$(b)	$^{231}_{90}$UY(b)
24 d	6.7 y	1 d
↓	↓	↓
$^{234}_{91}$UX$_2$(b)	$^{228}_{89}$MsTh$_2$(b)	$^{231}_{91}$Pa(a)
1 m	6 h	30000 y
↓	↓	↓
$^{234}_{92}$UII(a)	$^{228}_{90}$RdTh(a)	$^{227}_{89}$Ac(b)
300,000 y	2 y	13 y
↓	↓	↓
$^{230}_{90}$Io(a)	$^{224}_{88}$ThX(a)	$^{227}_{90}$RdAc(a)
80.000 y	3.6 d	19 d
↓	↓	↓
$^{226}_{88}$Ra(a)	$^{220}_{86}$Tn(a)	$^{223}_{88}$AcX(a)
1550 y	55 s	11 d
↓	↓	↓
$^{222}_{86}$Rn(a)	$^{216}_{84}$ThA(a)	$^{219}_{86}$An(a)
4 d	0.1 s	4 s
↓	↓	↓
$^{218}_{84}$RaA(a)	$^{212}_{82}$ThB(b)	$^{215}_{84}$AcA(a)
3 m	10 h	
↓	↓	↓
$^{214}_{82}$RaB(b)	$^{212}_{83}$ThC(a,b)	$^{211}_{82}$AcB(b)
27 m	1 h	35 m
↓		↓
$^{214}_{83}$RaC(a,b)		$^{211}_{83}$AcC(a,b)
20 m		2 m

Uranium branch: $^{210}_{81}$RaC"(b) 1 m ↙ $^{214}_{83}$RaC'(a) ↙ → $^{210}_{82}$RaD(b)

Thorium branch: $^{208}_{81}$ThC"(b) 3 m ← $^{212}_{84}$ThC'(a) → $^{208}_{82}$Pb

Actinium branch: $^{207}_{81}$AcC"(b) 5 m ↙ $^{211}_{84}$AcC'(a) ↙ → $^{207}_{82}$Pb

Uranium series (cont.)	Thorium series (cont.)	Actinium series (cont.)
$^{210}_{82}$RaD(b), 22 y	$^{208}_{82}$Pb	$^{207}_{82}$Pb
↓	stable	stable
$^{210}_{83}$RaE(b), 5 d	(THORIUMLEAD)	(ACTINIUMLEAD)
↓		
$^{210}_{84}$RaF(a), 140 d		
↓		
$^{206}_{82}$Pb		
stable		
(URANIUMLEAD)		

The symbols are those generally used for the radioactive products but it should be remembered that they all are isotopes of elements listed under (1). The atomic number indicates the element of which the radioactive product is an isotope; for instance, RaA, ThA and AcA which have atomic number 84 are all isotopes of the element polonium. The letter (a) and (b) indicate whether alpha or beta rays are emitted. Sometimes (e.g. in RaC) either an alphaparticle *or* an electron may be emitted; this is an example of competitive nuclear reactions (see p. 122) of comparable probability. The figures below the notation of the radioelement give its half value period (y = years, d = days, h = hours, m = minutes, s = seconds). If no figure is given, this means that the half value period is a very small fraction of a second. It is now established that the actinium series starts with U.235 and not, as was formerly believed, with protactinium. It is, of course, somewhat illusory to speak of the "start" of a series since the newly discovered transuranic elements are in turn parents of the radioelements listed below.

(4) High Speed Particles.

In order to carry out nuclear reactions, particles of high speed are required which can penetrate into the nuclei. A stone will gather speed when falling; it is accelerated by the gravitational field of the earth which acts on its mass. This method of acceleration is unsuitable for nuclear particles but they can be speeded up by allowing them to "fall" in an electric field which acts on their charge. A proton brought between a positively and negatively charged plate will "fall" towards the negative plate. Its final speed depends on the voltage between the plates, and in order to get protons fast enough to penetrate into nuclei, very high voltages (about 1 million volts or more) must be employed. Special generators for these high voltages had to be developed. Since the handling of very high voltage is difficult, machines have been developed in which the particle is made to fall again and again through the same (small) electric field. The most ingenious apparatus of this type is the cyclotron. So far positively charged particles only have been used. Electrons, in order to be effective for nuclear bombardment, have to be given almost the speed of light and this presents peculiar difficulties. However, a new instrument, called the betatron, has recently been developed which is capable of accelerating electrons to these high velocities. Neutrons, having no electric charge, cannot be accelerated by any of these methods. High speed neutrons employed in nuclear physics are the products of nuclear reactions started by bombardment with charged particles. Like the alpha-particles used in Rutherfords early experiments, these neutrons are accelerated by the forces acting within the atomic nuclei.

(5) Detection of Nuclear Particles.

All the methods used for the detection of fast particles issuing from nuclear reactions are based on the ability of these particles to tear away electrons from other atoms. This process is called "ionisation" (see pp. 16 and 84). One such method (the cloud chamber, p. 84) has already been mentioned. Another important detector is the Geiger-Müller counter which registers the passage of a charged particle by means of an electric impulse. A permanent record of particle tracks can be obtained by allowing the particles to pass through a photographic emulsion. Recent improvements in the type of emulsion used are likely to give this method wide applicability. Neutrons do not cause ionisation directly but they can be detected by their collisions with other nuclei which in turn produce ionisation (see p. 85).

GLOSSARY.

ALPHA-PARTICLE: Nucleus of helium atom.

ATOM: The smallest unit of a chemical element.

ATOMIC NUMBER: The number of protons in the nucleus (equal to the number of outer electrons) which determines the chemical properties of the atom.

BETA-RAYS: Electrons ejected from atomic nuclei.

BOHR ORBITS: Orbits of rotation around the nucleus assigned to the electrons in the Bohr-Rutherford model.

CAUSALITY: The conception that a (fully defined) cause can result in *only one* (predictable) effect.

CHAIN REACTION: A self-propagating release of energy.

CHEMICAL REACTION: A change involving the outermost electrons of atoms.

CLASSICAL PHYSICS: A system of physics which, in contradistinction to quantum-mechanics and relativity, is based on the observations of every day experience.

COHESIVE FORCES: The forces which act between like molecules or atoms in solids and liquids (see footnote p. 88).

COMPOUND NUCLEUS: A target nucleus containing the original particles as well as the bombarding particle. (See also: Unstable nucleus.)

DECAY: The natural breaking up of radioactive elements.

DIFFRACTION: Deviation suffered by a train of waves when encountering obstacles comparable in size with the wave-length.

DISINTEGRATION: The breaking up of a nucleus.

ELECTRIC ATTRACTION AND REPULSION: a force acting between *electric charges*.

ELECTRON: Elementary particle with negative (or positive) electric charge 1 and atomic weight 1/1840.

ELECTRON CLOUD: Electrons surrounding the nucleus.

ELECTRON SHELLS: Subdivisions of the electron cloud.

ELEMENT: A substance entirely composed of like atoms.

ELEMENTARY PARTICLES: The ultimate, indivisible particles of matter.

ENERGY STORE: A physical system from which energy can be released.

ENERGY TROUGH: Analogue representing the energy of a particle or of a physical system as a level in a trough filled with water.

EXCHANGE FORCE: A quantum-mechanical force the action of which is confined to atomic dimensions.

GAMMA-RAYS: Electro-magnetic rays of very short wave-length which are emitted in nuclear reactions.

GRAVITY: A force acting between *masses*.

HALF VALUE PERIOD: The time after which half the number of atoms of any particular radioactive element have disintegrated.

INTERDETERMINACY: The fundamental impossibility of determining the place and speed of a particle within a lower limit set by Planck's constant.

INTERFERENCE: The interaction between two or more trains of waves.

IONS: Electrically charged atoms.

ISOTOPES: Nuclei of equal atomic number but of different weights.

KILOWATT-HOUR: A measure of energy.

MASS DEFECT: The loss of mass suffered by a particle which has given off energy.

MASS SPECTOGRAPH: An instrument which separates isotopes and determines their weight.

MESON: A short lived elementary particle with (+ or −) charge 1 and atomic weight of about 1/10.

MODERATOR: A substance which reduces the speed of neutrons in a chain reaction pile.

MOLECULE: The smallest unit of a chemical compound.

NEUTRON: An uncharged elementary particle of atomic weight 1.

NUCLEAR REACTION: A change involving the elementary particles in the nucleus.

NUCLEUS (PLURAL: NUCLEI): The central core of the atom.

PHOTON: A quantum of radiant energy.

PILE: A device permitting controlled nuclear chain reactions.

PLANCK'S CONSTANT: A universal constant (energy x time) expressing the order of magnitude of quantum phenomena.

POSITRON: Positive electron.

PROTON: An elementary particle with charge $+1$ and atomic weight 1.

QUANTUM (PLURAL: QUANTA): The smallest amount of energy which can be given off or taken up in a particular physical process.

QUANTUM-MECHANICS (WAVE-MECHANICS); A system of physics (of particular importance in atomic dimensions) which takes into account the discontinuous nature of energy changes.

RADIATION: Energy transport by electro-magnetic waves.

RADIOACTIVITY: The spontaneous disintegration of nuclei.

RELATIVITY: The extension of classical physics to high velocities.

RESONANCE CAPTURE: The quantum-mechanical capture by a nucleus of a particle of a particular velocity.

STABLE STATE: The state of a physical system in which it does not undergo spontaneous changes.

TRANSURANIC ELEMENTS: Elements with atomic numbers higher than 92.

TRIGGER ACTION: A method of releasing stored energy.

UNSTABLE NUCLEUS: A nucleus which by emitting one or more particles or gamma-rays will relapse into a stable state of lower energy.
(*Note:* In fig. 29, p. 120 we have, somewhat arbitrarily, made a distinction between compound nuclei, which emit a heavy particle and "unstable" nuclei which emit electrons, in order to denote the degree of instability.)

X-RAYS: Short electromagnetic waves.

READING LIST.

Books marked with an asterisk are more advanced and require some knowledge of mathematics.

E. N. da C. Andrade, *THE MECHANISM OF NATURE*, G. Bell & Sons, 1936.

——————— ———————, *THE ATOM*, Nelson, 1936.

N. Bohr, *ATOMIC THEORY AND THE DESCRIPTION OF NATURE*, Cambridge University Press, 1934.

M. Born, *THE RESTLESS UNIVERSE*, Blackie & Son, 1935.

Sir C. G. Darwin, *THE NEW CONCEPTIONS OF MATTER*, G. Bell & Sons, 1931.

J. G. Daunt, *ELECTRONS IN ACTION*, Sigma Books, 1946.

D. S. Evans, *FRONTIERS OF ASTRONOMY*, Sigma Books, 1946.

* N. Feather, *AN INTRODUCTION TO NUCLEAR PHYSICS*, Cambridge University Press, 1936.

G. Gamow, *THE BIRTH AND DEATH OF THE SUN*, Macmillan, 1941.

* R. W. Gurney, *ELEMENTARY QUANTUM MECHANICS*, Cambridge University Press, 1934.

A. Haas, *THE WORLD OF ATOMS*, Chapman & Hall, 1937.

* W. Heitler, *ELEMENTARY WAVE MECHANICS*, Oxford University Press, 1945.

L. Infeld, *THE WORLD IN MODERN SCIENCE*, Victor Gollancz, 1934.

Sir James Jeans, *THE NEW BACKGROUND OF SCIENCE*, Cambridge University Press, 1934.

R. Millikan, *ELECTRONS (+ AND −), PROTONS, PHOTONS, NEUTRONS AND COSMIC RAYS*, Cambridge University Press, 1935.

C. Moller and A. Rasmussen, *THE WORLD AND THE ATOM*, Allen & Unwin, 1940.

* N. F. Mott, *AN OUTLINE OF WAVE MECHANICS*, Cambridge University Press, 1930.

* E. Pollard and W. N. Davidson, *APPLIED NUCLEAR PHYSICS*, Chapman & Hall, 1945.

M. Ruhemann, *POWER*, Sigma Books, 1946.

J. K. Robertson, *ATOMIC ARTILLERY AND THE ATOMIC BOMB*, Van Nostrand, 1945.

H. D. Smyth, *ATOMIC ENERGY FOR MILITARY PURPOSES*, Princeton University Press, 1945; reprinted H.M. Stationery Office.

STATEMENTS RELATING TO THE ATOMIC BOMB, H.M. Stationery Office, 1945.

A. K. Solomon, *WHY SMASH ATOMS,* Penguin Books, 1945.

H. A. Wilson, *THE MYSTERIES OF THE ATOM,* Chapman & Hall, 1934.

Accounts of current developments in science will be found in the Periodicals *NATURE* (Macmillan) and *DISCOVERY* (Empire Press).

INDEX.